Classic Brain Puzzlers

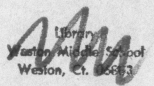

Classic Brain Puzzlers

PHILIP J. CARTER & KEN A. RUSSELL

WARD LOCK

A WARD LOCK BOOK

First published in the UK 1995 by
Ward Lock
Wellington House
125 Strand
London WC2R 0BB

A Cassell imprint

Distributed in the United States by Sterling Publishing Co. Inc.
387 Park Avenue South, New York, NY 10016-8810

A British Library Cataloguing in Publication Data block for
this book may be obtained from the British Library.

ISBN 0 7063 7231 X

Designed and typeset by Ben Cracknell
Printed and bound in Great Britain by
Caledonian International Book Manufacturing Ltd, Glasgow

– CONTENTS –

Acknowledgements ... 6

About Mensa ... 7

Introduction ... 9

Famous Puzzle Compilers ... 11

Questions ... 13

Puzzles are Fun ... 15

Complexities ... 26

The Old Favourites ... 38

Visual Puzzles ... 43

Classic Mathematical Puzzles ... 51

Word Play ... 60

Mighty Brainbenders ... 71

Classic Kickself ... 78

Perplexities ... 84

Answers ... 93

– ACKNOWLEDGEMENTS –

We are indebted to our wives, both named Barbara, for their continued enthusiastic support for all of our projects. Our special thanks go to Lynn Moore for her contribution in typing the manuscript.

– ABOUT MENSA –

M ENSA IS A SOCIAL CLUB for which membership is accepted from all persons with an IQ (Intelligence Quotient) of 148 or above on the Cattell scale of intelligence. This represents the top 2 per cent of the population. Therefore, one person in 50 is capable of passing the entrance test, which consists of a series of intelligence tests.

Mensa is the Latin word for 'table'. We are a round-table society in which all members are of equal standing. There are three aims: social contact among intelligent people; research in psychology; and the identification and fostering of intelligence.

Mensa is an International Society and has 110 000 members of all occupations: clerks, doctors, lawyers, policemen, industrial workers, teachers, nurses and so on.

UK
British Mensa Ltd
Mensa House
St John's Square
Wolverhampton
WV2 4AH

INTERNATIONAL
Mensa International Ltd
15 The Ivories
6–8 Northampton Street
London
N1 2HY

USA
American Mensa Ltd
2626 E14 Street
Brooklyn
NY 11235–3992

AUSTRALIA
Australian Mensa Inc.
PO BOX 519
Mona Vale
NSW   2103

– INTRODUCTION –

EVERY BOOK OF CLASSIC PUZZLES relies heavily on the genius of past masters, and this book is no exception. Riddles and puzzles have been propounded from biblical days, when Samson, in Judges XIV:14, asked the Philistines to solve the riddle: 'Out of the eater came forth meat and out of the strong came forth sweetness', right up to modern times with such puzzle masters as Martin Gardner and the 'king of word play', the late Dmitri Borgmann.

The zenith of puzzle compiling was, we believe, reached during the latter part of the nineteenth century with Lewis Carroll and Sam Loyd, and was carried on into the first half of the twentieth century by H.E. Dudeney and Hubert Phillips. These four giants of puzzledom were responsible for many new innovations, and we feature several examples of their work throughout this book.

The most difficult part of compiling a collection of Classic Brain Puzzlers is what to leave out. Deciding whether one brain-teaser is 'greater' than another has to be subjective, and we have tried to present as varied a selection of different types of puzzles as possible, and of varying degrees of difficulty, to give a flavour of the range of puzzles compiled throughout history.

We hope you will regard it as an entertaining, but at the same time serious and important, collection, which will be part of the process of passing such classic puzzles down from one generation to another.

– FAMOUS PUZZLE COMPILERS –

As MENTIONED in the Introduction, the four giants of puzzledom whose work is featured in this book are Lewis Carroll, Sam Loyd, H.E. Dudeney and Hubert Phillips. Below are some brief biographical details on each of them.

Sam Loyd

Sam Loyd was born in Philadelphia on 30 January 1841 but moved to New York in 1844. He studied to be an engineer and as a youth frequented a chess club, where his interest in compiling started. By 1858 he was hailed as the leading American composer of chess problems. He was only seventeen when he invented the Trick Mules, which he later sold to P.T. Barnum, and he was also responsible for many other famous puzzles, such as the 14–15 Puzzle and the Get off the Earth Puzzle, both of which are featured later in this book. By the late 1890s he was making more money from compiling puzzles than in his regular employment, and he became a full-time professional compiler. After his death his work was collected by his son into the *Cyclopedia of Puzzles*, which was published in 1914.

Henry Ernest Dudeney

H.E. Dudeney, who was born in 1847 in Mayfield, Sussex, was Sam Loyd's British counterpart. The two men corresponded frequently, and there is no doubt that they exchanged ideas and did not hesitate to use or modify each other's inventions. Dudeney contributed puzzles to *Strand*'s Tit-bits column under the pseudonym of Sphinx, and he was soon given his own column, Perplexities. Dudeney believed that puzzle-solving was an intellectual process of the highest order and that no one could be more clear-thinking and logical than one who constructed such works. Among his publications are *The Canterbury Puzzles* (1917), *The World's Best Word Puzzles* (1925) and *Amusements in Mathematics*, which has a preface dated 25 March 1917 and which is a marvellous collection of arithmetical, algebraical, geometrical, point and line, route, chessboard and magic square problems.

Lewis Carroll

Born Charles Lutwidge Dodgson at Daresbury, Cheshire, in 1832, he was educated at Rugby and Oxford, took orders in 1861 and was a lecturer of mathematics at Christ College, Oxford, from 1855 until 1881. He wrote the children's classic *Alice's Adventures in Wonderland* (1865) and its sequel *Through the Looking Glass* (1872) for the second daughter, Alice Liddell, of the head of his Oxford college. He had a lifetime obsession for all types of puzzles and was responsible for many original puzzles and new innovations, including Doublets (1879) and the Game of Logic (1866), both of which are featured later in this book.

Hubert Phillips

Hubert Phillips is still remembered by many people who heard him on radio quizzes. He was born in 1891, took a first class degree in history at Oxford, served in the army throughout the First World War, taught Economics at Bristol University and was Director of Extra-Mural Studies, Secretary to the Liberal Industrial Enquiry and secretary and advisor to the Liberal Parliamentary Party. He was well known by several pseudonyms, including Dogberry of the *News Chronicle*'s magazine page and Caliban of the *New Statesman*, and he was the compiler of thousands of mathematical and inferential puzzles as well as of crosswords, quizzes and ciphers. He was also a prolific writer of epigrams, parodies and satirical verse. Among his many publications are *Caliban's Problem Book*, *The Complete Book of Card Games*, the Penguin *Hoyle*, *Brush up Your Wits* and *My Best Puzzles in Mathematics*. He also published over a hundred crime-problem stories and a novel, *Charteris Royal*. He was an accomplished player of contract bridge, captaining England in 1937 and 1938.

Questions

– PUZZLES ARE FUN –

*'A quiz should serve to give pleasure to those
who take part in it: it is not an examination.'*

THE ABOVE WAS WRITTEN by Hubert Phillips in June
1947 as part of the foreword to one of his quiz books
published by Ptarmigan Books called *Who Wrote That?*, and
it is exactly our philosophy in respect of both quizzes and
puzzles. The late Isaac Asimov once commented that it is
extremely dull simply to pick up a book of puzzles and
attempt to do them one after the other. We agree that the fun
comes from dipping into the book and attempting any puzzle
that takes your fancy. The more difficult it is to answer, the
more fun it is, especially if you can arrive at the correct
answer.

We can think of no better example of a fun puzzle than
Sam Loyd's Trick Mules Puzzle, Q1, which is, in fact, deceptively difficult. The object is to cut the two dotted lines indi-
cated by the arrow heads and to re-assemble the three
resultant pieces so that the two jockeys are riding the
mules. The puzzle was sold by Loyd to the American show-
man P.T. Barnum (of Barnum and Bailey's Circus fame) who
sold the puzzle at $1 each, and it is said that as a result
Loyd earned some $10,000 in royalties.

Sam Loyd was a master at compiling puzzles that
appeared so simple to solve that people felt compelled to
attempt them, only to find that they would spend hours
unsuccessfully trying to figure them out.

You will find several other puzzles in the same vein as
you dip in and out of this book. Good luck, happy solving
and have fun.

CUT THE CARD on the dotted lines (into three pieces only) and lay them so that each mule has a correct rider.

In this book we have included several chess-based problems. This, the first, was devised around 1900 by Boris Kordemsky, the author of *The Moscow Puzzles*.

HOW CAN a knight capture all 16 pawns in 16 moves?

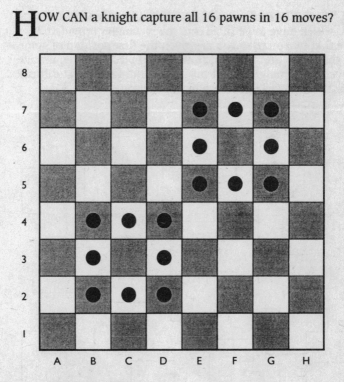

The knight's move in chess

Jigsaw puzzles can be fiendishly difficult, as in the case of this puzzle, which one of the authors recently bought in an antique shop in York.

THE PUZZLE consists of 20 differently shaped pieces, which have to be fitted into the rectangles provided. In the first two puzzles you are given the first position of some of the pieces and told which numbered pieces are required to cover the rectangle completely. In the third and most difficult puzzle no pieces have been placed for you.

1. Insert 2, 3, 5, 9, 10, 13, 14, 15, 16 and 18

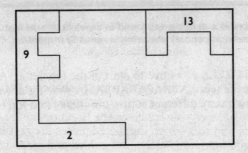

2. Insert 3, 6, 7, 8, 10, 12, 14, 15, 17 and 19

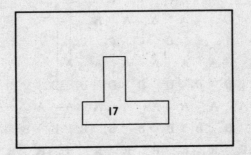

3. Insert 1, 4, 7, 11, 13, 14, 15, 17, 19 and 20

Abracadabra is a magic word found in amulets. It was featured in a second-century poem by Serenus Sammonicus.

IN THIS PUZZLE you have to start at the top letter, A, and spell out the word ABRACADABRA, by moving downwards. How many different routes are there from top to bottom?

```
                    A
                 B     B
              R     R     R
           A     A     A     A
        C     C     C     C     C
     A     A     A     A     A     A
  D     D     D     D     D     D     D
A     A     A     A     A     A     A     A
  B     B     B     B     B     B     B     B     B
R     R     R     R     R     R     R     R     R     R
A   A   A   A   A   A   A   A   A   A   A
```

This is a great puzzle, which was devised by Sam Loyd. In it he relates the story of Professor Von Schafskoppen, the distinguished naturalist, who scours the country in search of the legendary hoop-snake, which travels around the countryside at great speed by taking the end of its tail in its mouth and rolling along the ground in the shape of a hoop. Eventually the professor finds a petrified hoop-snake, still with its tail in its mouth. To facilitate transportation, he cuts the snake into 10 pieces and returns to his laboratory. Unfortunately, he has since been trying to find how to put the hoop-snake back together again correctly.

CAN YOU ARRANGE the 10 pieces so that the snake will bite its tail? After placing the tail correctly in the snake's mouth, there are 40,320 different ways of putting the remaining eight pieces together, but only one of these will produce the desired solution.

The following logic puzzle was compiled by Hubert Phillips for his book *Brush up Your Wits*.

'I'VE JUST BEEN STAYING,' writes Toady, 'at the court of King Jovial of Hilaria. Everything there is delightfully informal.

'We dined, for instance, at a Round Table (thus avoiding difficult questions of precedence). There were 12 of us at the table – six husbands and their wives – and the rule was that no husband sat next to his wife, but was separated from her by the same number of places. For instance, Queen Cilly sat opposite to Lady Peekaboo, while the Duke of Dull Ness sat three places to the Queen's left. I was three places to the duchess's right, the Marchioness of Muttonfat was two places from the Queen, while my wife sat opposite Lady Parsley.'

Draw a plan of the table showing how the 12 diners were seated.

CAN YOU SOLVE the following brain-teaser? It is by
Johann Christoph Friedrich von Schiller (1759–1805),
the German dramatist, poet and historian who compiled several riddles, which were contained in *Turandot* (1802) *and
Parabeln und Ratsel* (1803).

> For ages an edifice here has been found
>   It is not a dwelling it is not a fane;
> A horseman for hundreds of days may ride round,
>   Yet the end of the journey he ne'er can attain.
> Full many a century o'er it has pass'd,
>   The might of the storm and of time it defies;
> 'Neath the rainbow of Heaven stands free to the last, –
>   In the ocean it dips, and soars up to the skies.
> It was not a vain glory bade its erection
>   It serves as a refuge, a shield or protection;
> Its like on the earth never yet has been known
>   And yet by man's hand it is fashion'd alone.

A WINE MERCHANT had a dishonest employee who regularly helped himself to bottles of wine. Eventually the merchant decided to catch out the employee. He had 28 green bottles of wine in his store and arranged them as shown in the diagram so that there were nine bottles along each side. The employee, however, realized that the trap had been set, so when he took away four bottles he re-arranged the remainder so that there were still nine bottles along each side. Later he returned and took four more bottles and again re-arranged the remainder so that there were nine bottles on each side. How did he do this?

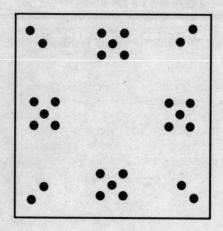

A REBUS is an arrangement of pictures, letters or symbols to suggest a word, name or phrase. They were fashionable around 100 years ago and have recently become very popular again. This one was compiled by Sam Loyd. What does it represent?

Q10   **MARRIED COUPLES**   A96

This simple little puzzle is based on a logic puzzle known to be at least 60 years old.

A MAN leaves £10,000 in his will, to which there are six separate beneficiaries – his three sons and their wives. The three wives in total receive £3,960 of which Janice gets £100 more than Susan and Helen gets £100 more than Janice. Of the sons, James gets twice as much as his wife, Alec gets the same as his wife and Peter gets 50 per cent more than his wife. Who is married to whom?

– COMPLEXITIES –

THE COMMON FEATURE shared by all the puzzles in this section is that they involve complex solutions. They are not the type of puzzle you can solve in an instant and it is necessary to sit down with a pencil and paper and work your way through each puzzle stage by stage in a logical manner to arrive at a structured solution. They are the type of puzzle in which your time and patience are rewarded with a great deal of satisfaction when eventually you arrive at a correct solution – a philosphy that is reinforced in one of the author's 1986 puzzles, reproduced here as Q11.

B EGIN AT THE TOP left-hand corner and travel to the bottom right-hand corner by moving from letter to letter, vertically, horizontally or diagonally, to unscramble a hidden message. You have to visit each square once only, and there are no redundant squares.

W	E	S	I	H	B	E	Y	D	D
C	H	S	F	S	T	D	O	N	O
C	U	E	P	U	E	E	T	B	U
S	N	L	L	U	V	T	I	Q	A
U	Y	Y	Z	O	E	T	I	L	U
C	O	Z	R	L	S	E	N	A	N
Y	O	L	P	P	O	I	O	P	D
O	E	M	E	F	A	T	A	T	I
W	U	L	V	D	N	I	R	N	E
I	L	H	A	E	T	E	M	C	E

The following logic puzzle was devised by Hubert Phillips.

MESSRS DRAFTSMAN, Etcher, Musician and Sculptor are a draftsman, an etcher, a musician and a sculptor. Of none, however, are the name and vocation the same. The draftsman is not the namesake of Mr Musician's vocation. The etcher is neither Mr Sculptor, nor the namesake of Mr Etcher's vocation.

Can you say what Mr Etcher's vocation is?

This puzzle was devised by H.E. Dudeney.

INSIDE A RECTANGULAR ROOM, which is 30 feet long and 12 feet wide and high, a spider is at a point in the middle of one of the end walls, 1 foot from the ceiling, at point A, and a fly is on the opposite wall, 1 foot from the floor in the centre, at point B.

What is the shortest distance that the spider may crawl in order to reach the fly, which remains stationary?

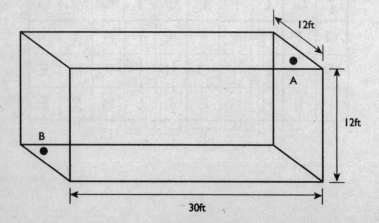

This puzzle was sent to one of the authors several years ago by
Doug Pattinson, a Mensa member from Leeds, UK. It was dated
1881 and had been handed down through Mr Pattinson's family.
Just to prove it worked in practice, Mr Pattinson constructed the
puzzle in wood as a gift for the author. See if you can work out the
answer using a pencil and paper. Alternatively, the craftspeople
among you may try to emulate Mr Pattinson by constructing the
puzzle yourselves. The instructions given here are as they were
originally written.

HAVING SIX PIECES of wood, bone or metal, made of the
same length as in No. 6, in the figures below, and each
piece of the same size as No. 7. It is required to construct a
cross, with six arms, from these pieces, in such a manner
that it shall not be displaced when thrown upon the floor.

The shaded parts of each figure represents the parts that
are cut *out* of the wood, and each piece marked *a* is sup-
posed to be facing the reader, while the pieces marked *b* are
the *right* side of each piece turned over *towards* the left, so
as to face the reader. No. 7 represents the end of each piece
of wood, &c., and is given to show the dimensions

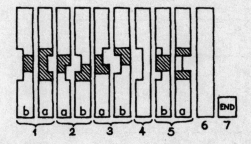

It was not until the seventeenth-century, when the French mathematician Blaise Pascal formulated the first rules relating to probability, that people were really aware that they existed. Until then, gambling had been governed by gut feeling and comparison of results.

HERE IS A TYPICAL example of a puzzle based on the rules of probability. A total of 20 white balls and 30 black balls are placed in a box. What are the chances of drawing out in turn:

1. Black then white
2. White then black
3. White followed by white
4. Black followed by black?

The above should be treated as four separate puzzles – i.e., in puzzle 1 the black ball is drawn out and remains out and then the white ball is drawn out. All the balls are back in the bag for puzzle 2.

This puzzle was compiled by one of the authors in 1986.

I WON ALL THREE major knockout competitions at my golf club last year (wishful thinking), even though I was the only player unlucky enough to be drawn in both preliminary rounds.

Recently, our club statistician stopped me and said:'Do you know, I cubed the number of entrants for each competition and the last digit of each of the three resultant numbers is the same as your golf handicap and the sum of the three middle digits – i.e., the middle digit of each of the cube numbers – is the same as mine; also, the total number of rounds you have won is the same as your wife's handicap, which is exactly double your own handicap. Furthermore, the total number of matches played, including the end-of-season consolation event for players knocked out in the preliminary rounds, is the same as the age of Seth Arkwright, our surviving founder member.'

What are mine, my wife's and the club statistician's handicaps and how old is Seth Arkwright?

This puzzle is taken from *The Treviso Arithmetic* (1478).

THE HOLY FATHER sent a courier from Rome to Venice to reach Venice in 7 days. The Signoria of Venice sent a courier to Rome to reach Rome in 9 days. The distance was 250 miles.

In how many days will they meet?

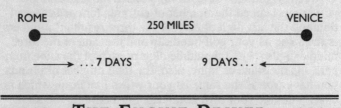

ROME   250 MILES   VENICE

——→ ...7 DAYS   9 DAYS... ←——

Here is another puzzle, dating from around 1900, by Boris Kordemsky, author of *The Moscow Puzzles*.

ON THE MOSCOW–LENINGRAD TRAIN are three passengers named Ivanov, Petrov and Sidorov. By coincidence, the engine driver, the fireman and the guard have the same last names.

1. Passenger Ivanov lives in Moscow.
2. The guard lives halfway between Moscow and Leningrad.
3. The passenger with the same name as the guard lives in Leningrad.
4. The passenger who lives nearest the guard earns exactly three times as much per month as the guard.
5. Passenger Petrov earns 200 roubles a month.
6. Sidorov (a member of the crew) recently beat the fireman at billiards.

What is the engine driver's last name?

In 1885 Lewis Carroll published a series of puzzles under the general heading *A Tangled Tale*, which was divided into 10 chapters called 'knots'. The puzzles were incorporated into a narrative and each knot had to be untangled by readers, with whom he built up a lively correspondence. The following puzzle, which appeared in Knot One, is entitled 'Excelsior'.

TWO TRAVELLERS spend from 3 o'clock till 9 in walking along a level road, up a hill, and home again: their pace on the level being 4 miles an hour, up hill 3 and down hill 6. Find the distance walked: also (within half an hour) the time of reaching the top of the hill.

The following puzzle was compiled by Hubert Phillips and was published in his book *Brush up Your Wits*.

THE OLD MARKET TOWN of Much Giggling has a town council of nine members. These are Messrs Baker, Butcher, Brewer, Carter, Draper, Ironmonger, Painter, Saddler and Smith. These gentlemen are (not necessarily respectively) a baker, a butcher, a brewer, a carter, a draper, an ironmonger, a painter, a saddler and a smith.

The saddler is the ironmonger's father-in-law. Mr Saddler is engaged to the painter's only daughter, who has already rejected Mr Saddler's rivals, the draper and the baker. Mr Carter's daughter partners her fiancé at tennis. Mr Draper, who is a bachelor, has succeeded the namesake of his vocation as captain of the cricket team. Mr Smith shares an allotment with his son-in-law. The draper's father is a brother of the wife of Mr Baker. The brewer and the carter are married to each other's sisters. No councillor has more than one daughter; two councillors have one each. The brewer is the namesake of the vocation of the namesake of the vocation of Mr Carter, and the carter is the namesake of the vocation of the namesake of the vocation of Mr Smith.

Identify the vocation of each of the nine councillors.

This cross-number was devised by H.E. Dudeney.

Across

1 A square number
4 A square number
5 A square number
8 The digits sum to 35
11 Square root of 30 across
13 A square number
14 A square number
15 Square of 36 across
17 Square of half 11 across
18 Three similar figures
19 Product of 4 across
   and 33 across
21 A square number
22 5 times 5 across
23 All digits alike except
   the central one
25 Square of 2 down
27 See 20 down
28 A fourth power
29 Sum of 18 + 31 across
31 A triangular number
33 1 more than 4 times
   36 across
34 Digits sum to 18
   and the 3 middle
   numbers are 3
36 An odd number
37 All digits even except
   one, and their sum is 29
39 A fourth power
40 A cube power
41 Twice a square

Down

1 Reads both ways alike
2 Square root of 28 across
3 Sum of 17 across
   + 21 across
4 Digits sum to 19
5 Digits sum to 26
6 Sum of 14 + 33 across
7 A cube number
9 A cube number
10 A square number
12 Digits sum to 30
14 All similar figures
16 Sum of digits is 12 down
18 All similar digits
   excepting first
20 Sum of 17 + 27 across
21 Multiple of 19
22 A square number
24 A square number
26 Square of 18 across
28 A fourth power of 4 across
29 Twice 15 across
30 A triangular number
32 Digits sum to 20
34 6 times 21 across
35 A cube number
37 A square number
38 A cube number

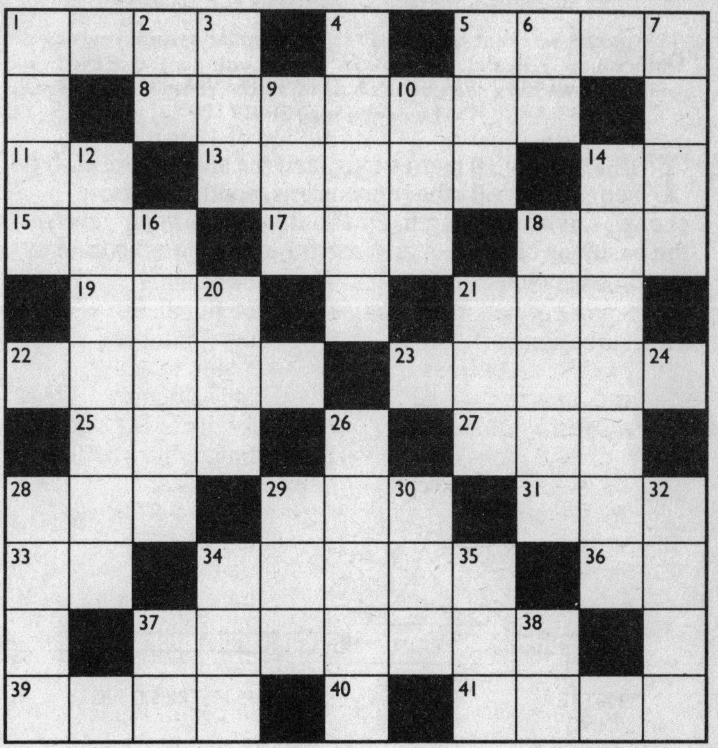
1
2
3
4
5
6
7
8
9
10
11
12
13
14
15
16
17
18
19
20
21
22
23
24
25
26
27
28
29
30
31
32
33
34
35
36
37
38
39
40
41

This puzzle was sent to us by a Mensa member several years ago.
Unfortunately, he did not know its source, but it is one of the best
of its kind we have seen, so it's hats off to the compiler, who ever
he or she may be.

THE TRAIN is 10 metres long, and the coaches are each 5
metres long. All other dimensions, apart from those
shown, can be any length. By shunting you have to reverse
the positions of coach A and coach B and return the train to
its starting point.

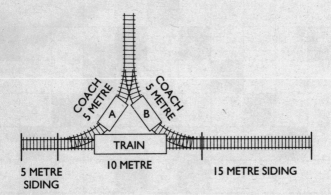

Here is another puzzle that was included by Hubert Phillips
in his book *Brush up Your Wits*.

I HAVE HAD a number of letters from some young friends
of mine, in which they all refer to a sort of beauty competition they have all been in.

From Basil: I've been acting as one of the judges to choose
Miss Joyville. Six girls competed, and it was agreed that the
ten judges should each have ten votes to distribute as he
liked among the competitors, but that as a safeguard against
'plumping' none of us would give a 'duck' to more than one
competitor. Annette was undoubtedly the winner – at any
rate eight of us thought so. But the judging was a puzzling
business, and in my view there was nothing to choose
between the rest of the competitors.

From Hamish: I didn't quite agree with Basil; I thought that
Fern was every bit as attractive as Annette, but I did agree
with him about the rest, and Victor thought that some other
girl shared Annette's pedestal.

From Fern: Annette got four time as many votes as I did;
three of the judges gave me no votes at all, and Jim, my
fiancé, only bracketed me second with Sonia; even so, she
did better than I did, though she got no votes at all from
either Alec or Stephen and only one from Lionel.

From Mayblossom: I only got third place. Teddy – the
blighter – gave me no marks at all, and even Victor gave
Annette one more than me.

From Everard: Annette was an easy winner. I thought her
worth more than all the others put together, and Lionel was
nearly as enthusiastic. But no two of us distributed his votes
numerically in exactly the same way. Geoffrey had the
strange idea of giving Sonia second place; in actual fact the
second place went to Helen.

From Prudence: I was rather a flop, but anyway Alec
thought me just as good as Mayblossom, and better than
Helen, and I'm bucked at beating Sonia.

Now, just how did those 10 judges distribute their votes?

– THE OLD FAVOURITES –

THE AUTHORS can recall many puzzles that they heard of as children. For example in the Frog in the Circle the question is posed: 'How many jumps does a frog require to make to get out of a circle if it starts in the centre, jumps half the radius with its first leap, then half the distance remaining, then half again, and so on?' The answer, of course, is that it never will escape from the circle no matter how agonizingly close to the circumference it reaches. A similar paradox was posed by the ancient Greek Zeno, around 450BC, in which he proposes that in a race between Achilles and the Tortoise, if Achilles gives a tortoise a start he cannot overtake it, for whenever he arrives where the tortoise was, it has already moved on.

There are scores of other old favourite classic puzzles, many of which have their origins deep in history and of which we present a small selection in this section.

IN MY LIBRARY is a three-volume encyclopedia. Taking it from the shelf one day I was annoyed to see that a bookworm had eaten its way in a straight line from the first page of volume 1 to the last page of volume 3. I measured the thickness of the books and found that each was 2¼ inches across, the pages being 2 inches thick and the covers ⅛ inch each.

How far had the bookworm travelled?

A LONG TIME AGO a farmer died and left 19 horses to be divided among his three sons. The eldest son was to inherit half, the next son was to have a quarter and the youngest son a fifth. However, the will stated that none of the horses was to be slaughtered to help in the division. While they were pondering how it was to be possible to divide 19 by 2, 4 or 5 parts without a remainder, a neighbouring farmer rode up, jumped off his horse and put it with the 19, making 20. Then he gave half (10) to the eldest brother, a quarter (5) to the second brother and a fifth (4) to the youngest brother. The 10, 5 and 4 horses made 19, the twentieth horse was returned to the neighbouring farmer, and he departed, having done his good deed for the day. The brothers were all happy with this but were never able to understand why.

What is the explanation? Why was it possible for the neighbour to add his own horse to the others, do the dividing exactly as required by the will and have his own horse returned to him at the end?

A SLUG is at the bottom of a well and decides to make his way to the top. He climbs up 3 feet each day, but then slips back 2 feet during his night-time slumber. The well is 20 feet deep. How long does it take the slug to get to the top?

Q27 THE BROKEN CLOCK FACE A82

T HIS CLOCK was dropped on the floor and the face broke into four pieces. When the bits were picked up it was noticed that the numbers on all four pieces added up to the same amount. What was the amount and what did each piece contain?

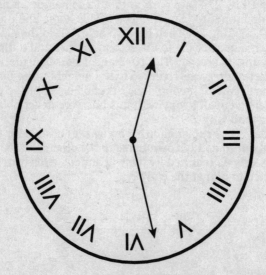

TWO FARM LABOURERS were arguing about a water butt. One said it was less than half-full and the other said it was more than half-full. To settle the argument they asked the farmer to adjudicate. Although there were no other implements or vessels at hand with which to measure the water the farmer was quickly able to determine who was correct. How did he do it?

The puzzle illustrated is a reproduction of a river crossing puzzle devised in 1910.

THREE LABOURERS and three capitalists must cross a river. However, as the labourers do not trust the capitalists they (the capitalists) cannot at any time outnumber the labourers on either side of the river. How do the six achieve the crossing as efficiently as possible – i.e., in the fewest possible number of moves – given that the boat holds only two people and, although all the labourers can row, only one of the capitalists can row.

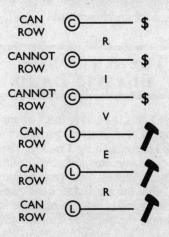

This puzzle dates from the eighth century.

A MAN HAS to take a wolf, a goat and a cabbage across a river. His rowing boat can take:

Man plus wolf, or
Man plus goat, or
Man plus cabbage.

If he takes the cabbage, the wolf will eat the goat. If he takes the wolf, the goat will eat the cabbage. How does he get the three across?

**This river crossing puzzle was compiled by
Claude-Jasper Batchet in 1612**

THREE JEALOUS HUSBANDS with their wives have to cross a river by rowing boat. The boat can carry only two persons at a time. Only three people out of the six can row. How can the six people cross the river so that none of the women shall be left in the company of any of the men, unless when her husband is present?

A 3-INCH LONG elastic band is fixed at one end. An ant crawls along it at the rate of 1 inch per minute. After 1 minute the band is stretched by 3 inches. The ant then crawls along at the same rate and after 1 minute the band is stretched a further 3 inches. This cycle continues at the end of each minute, until the ant reaches the end of the band. Assuming that the band is capable of being stretched so far, how long will it take the ant to reach the end?

– VISUAL PUZZLES –

PROBABLY THE FIRST visual puzzles we can all remember from childhood are the visual deception puzzles, of which we present several examples in this section, including Q33. There are, however, many other types of visual puzzle – matchstick puzzles, as in Q34, counting triangles, of which the one shown in Q35 was composed by one of the the authors in 1986, and mazes, such as the one shown here, which is taken from a book of designs for garden mazes, *Architectura Curiosa* by G.A. Boeckler, which was published in 1664.

WHICH IS the larger circle, A or B?

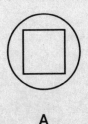

A

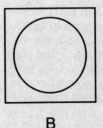

B

ADD FIVE MATCHES to make nine.

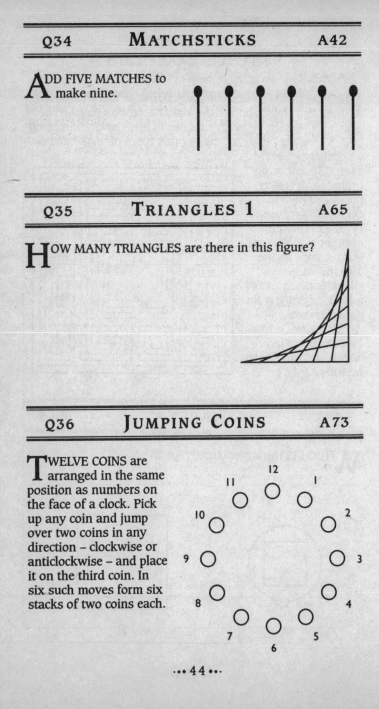

HOW MANY TRIANGLES are there in this figure?

TWELVE COINS are arranged in the same position as numbers on the face of a clock. Pick up any coin and jump over two coins in any direction – clockwise or anticlockwise – and place it on the third coin. In six such moves form six stacks of two coins each.

A REBUS is an arrangement of letters to indicate a word or phrase – for example, BBBBBB = bee line. The first of the 18 examples below is a classic rebus, many years old, and the answer that you are looking for is a quotation from Shakespeare. The remaining 17 were compiled by the authors between 1984 and 1993, and they may be a one–word answer or a well-known phrase or saying.

1 KIND	2 IIIIIIIIIII SSSSSSSSSS	3 (cascade of i's rising to I)
4 TOCCDUN	5 MEAS	6 RACT
7 NEMT	8 HYDE HYDE	9 BIBLE
10 R I A N B	11 TUASPRF	12 AS TAT EOF
13 JOL [2♦] SON	14 THE FIFTH	15 (dots forming : C)
16 LIS	17 AALLLL	18 GNINWOD

The following puzzle is attributed to Sir Isaac Newton and appeared in the book *Rational Amusement for Winter Evenings* by John Jackson, which was published in 1821.

THE OBJECT of the puzzle is to plant nine trees so that they form ten straight rows with three trees in every row.

● ● ●

● ● ●

● ● ●

THERE ARE MANY puzzles designed to deceive the eye. These three are typical examples, and you have to solve each one using the naked eye only.

1. Which of the two horizontal lines is longer?

2. These two strips were cut from a circle. Which is the longer piece?

3. In which of the figures, A or B, is the vertical line longer?

THIS DISSECTION PUZZLE is by H.E. Dudeney. Each hoof has to be cut into two pieces and the four resultant pieces re-assembled to form a circle.

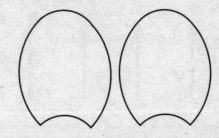

Q41   THE 36-COIN PUZZLE   A100

TAKE AWAY SIX COINS so that all the rows that are left contain an even number, whether reckoned vertically, horizontally or corner-to-corner.

ARRANGE THE SIX MATCHES to form four triangles.

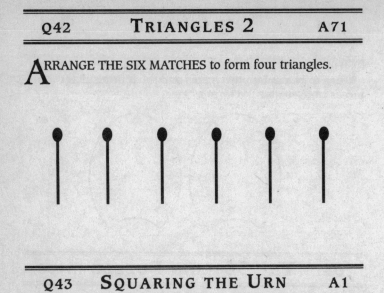

This puzzle dates back to the Ancient Egyptians.

DRAW TWO STRAIGHT LINES to cut the shaded section into three pieces that can be arranged to form a square.

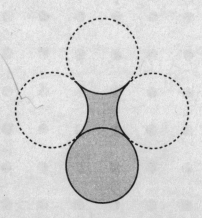

There are a number of dissection puzzles involving letters. This
example and Q45 involve assembling the letter H.

THIS PUZZLE was produced in the 1920s, and it is an adaptation of the classic letter T puzzle, with which many of you will be familiar. The object is to arrange the six pieces to form a letter H. It is a deceptively difficult puzzle.

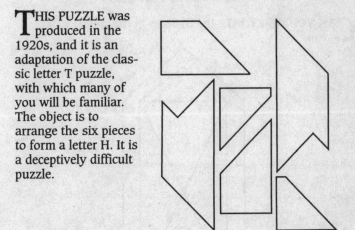

This puzzle was produced by N.K. Atlas of Paris in 1920. It calls for
a certain amount of ingenuity on the part of the solver.

CAN YOU ARRANGE the eight triangular pieces into the shape of a letter H?

This is a good example of a puzzle in which you have to draw around a figure without lifting your pencil from the paper and without going over any part twice. This particular puzzle is known to be at least 60 years old.

C AN YOU NEGOTIATE the 31 lines in the correct order?

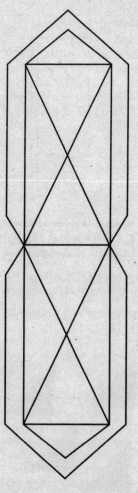

– CLASSIC MATHEMATICAL –
PUZZLES

IT WOULD NOT BE POSSIBLE to include every classic mathematical puzzle ever compiled in just one book, and at best all we can attempt to do is present a carefully chosen, typical and challenging selection.

In any book of classic puzzles the name Sam Loyd is always going to be at the forefront, and, as you will have already gathered, this book is no exception. He was responsible for many classic mathematical puzzles, of which one of the most famous is illustrated here, which he invented in the 1870s and called the 14–15 Puzzle in Puzzleland. It was to lead to the invention of many other sliding-block puzzles with which many of you will be familiar. The puzzle consisted of a square base in which 15 blocks were arranged in regular order, but with the 14 and 15 reversed. The object was to move the blocks about, one at a time, and to return them to their present positions, except that the error in the positions of 14 and 15 was corrected. In the words of Loyd, the puzzle 'drove the entire world crazy', and he offered a prize of $1,000 for the first correct solution.

1	2	3	4
5	6	7	8
9	10	11	12
13	15	14	

The money was never claimed, however, because, as Loyd already knew, there was no possible solution. He had realized that half the possible starting positions do not lead to a solution because re-arrangement of the blocks by sliding them only gives rise to an equal number of exchanges. He changed the position of 14 and 15 and challenged the solver to correct their positions but, since this is equivalent to only a single, uneven exchange of blocks, it was impossible. The mathematics of the puzzle is that there are over 600 billion arrangements of the blocks that can be made from the original position and there is an equal number that cannot be made. As Loyd himself put it: 'The original problem is impossible to solve except by such skulduggery as turning the 6 and 9 blocks upside down. One of the puzzle's peculiarities is that any such interchange involving two blocks immediately converts the puzzle to a solvable one. In fact, any odd number of interchanges has the same effect, whereas an even number leaves the puzzle unsolvable as before.'

On this occasion, however, Loyd did not have the last laugh. There was an amusing twist in the tail when Loyd applied to patent the puzzle. In those days it was necessary to present a working model of a device but when the Patent Commissioner was told that no solution existed he retorted: 'Then you can't have a patent. If the thing won't work, how can you file a working model of it!'

THE LABOURER'S PUZZLE

Here is another puzzle by H.E. Dudeney.

DURING ONE OF HIS RAMBLES, Professor Rackbrane chanced to come upon a man digging a deep hole.

'Good morning' he said. 'How deep is that hole?'

'Guess' replied the labourer. 'My height is exactly 5 feet 10 inches.'

'How much deeper are you going?' asked the Professor.

'I am going twice as deep,' was the answer, 'and then my head will be twice as far below ground as it is now above ground.'

Rackbrane now asks if you could tell how deep that hole would be when it was finished.

The following puzzle is the work of Nicolas Chuquet,
a French mathematician who wrote
Triparty en la science des nombres in 1484.

A CARPENTER agrees to work on the condition that he is
paid 2 units for every day that he works, while he for-
feits 3 units for every day that he does not work.

At the end of 30 days he finds that he has paid out exactly as much as he has received. How many days did he
work?

Q49 THE SOLDIER'S RETURN   A40

This is one of Lewis Carroll's best known brain teasers.

O N RETURN FROM the battlefield, the regiment is badly
battle-scarred. If 70 per cent of the soldiers have lost an
eye, 75 per cent have lost an ear, 85 per cent have lost a leg
and 80 per cent have lost an arm, what percentage at least
must have lost all four?

Q50   THE DIOPHANTINE   A55
SQUARES

Diophantus was a 3rd century AD Greek mathematician who
lived at Alexandria. Of his three known works, only six books of
his treatise on algebra, *Arithmetica*, have survived. The following
puzzle is one of the earliest problems in mathematics and was one
of several solved by Diophantus.

F ind three numbers such that their sum is a perfect
square, and the sum of any two is perfect square.

Can you find the three numbers, all of which are less than
500?

H.E. Dudeney included this puzzle in one of his books in 1917 and described it as 'a funny little age problem, by the late Sam Loyd, which has been very popular in the United States'.

THE COMBINED AGES of Mary and Ann are 44 years, and Mary is twice as old as Ann was when Mary was half as old as Ann will be when Ann is three times as old as Mary was when Mary was three times as old as Ann. How old is Mary? That is all, but can you work it out?

A. Henry Rhind, a Scottish Egyptologist purchased 'The Rhind Papyrus', a rich source of the work of Egyptian mathematicians. The papyrus, which is 18 feet 6 inches long and 13 inches wide, dates from 1650 BC. The writing covers both sides and includes the following puzzle.

THERE ARE SEVEN houses each containing seven cats, each cats kill seven mice, and each mouse would have eaten seven ears of spelt. Each ear of spelt would have produced seven hekats of grain. What is the total of all these?

This Ancient Chinese puzzle, which dates from the fourth century AD, is by Sun Tsu Suan-Ching.

'HOW MANY GUESTS are there?' said the official.

'I do not know,' said the cook, 'but every two used a dish for rice between them, every three used a dish for broth between them and every four used a dish for meat between them.'

There were 65 dishes in all. How many guests were there?

The Bhakshali Manuscript was found in 1881 in northwest India and dates from the third to the twelfth centuries. In it is the following puzzle.

20 men, women and children earn 20 coins between them.
Each man earns 3 coins
Each woman earns 1½ coins
Each child earns ½ coin

How many men women and children are there?

Puzzles in which numbers were replaced by letters first appeared thousands of years ago in Ancient China. Originally they were known as 'letter arithmetic', then 'cryptarithms' and, since 1955, 'alphametics'.

1. In the division sum below each letter stands for a different number. None of the digits in the divisor (135) occurs elsewhere in the sum, and there is no remainder. Can you complete the sum?

```
1 3 5 ) P H I L ( P P
        P I L
        ‾‾‾‾‾
        P I L
        P I L
        ‾‾‾‾‾
```

2. Here is another division sum, but this is more difficult.

```
M Y ) W O R D ( K E N
      N W
      ‾‾‾
      G R
      Y R
      ‾‾‾
      M D D
        R M
        ‾‾‾
          R
```

If you know a unique fact about a certain number it should be possible to construct a puzzle from it. This is one such puzzle, which was compiled by one of the authors in 1989.

A RICH COLLECTOR OF GOLD coins left a very complicated will giving instructions about how his gold coin collection (of fewer than 5,000 coins) was to be distributed among his ten children – five sons and five daughters – after his death. The instructions he gave were that first of all one gold coin was to be given to his butler, then exactly a fifth of those remaining had to go to his eldest son. Another coin was then given to the butler, then exactly a fifth of those still remaining went to his next eldest son. This procedure was repeated exactly until all his five sons had received a share, and the butler had been given five gold coins. Then, after the fifth son had taken his share the gold coins still remaining were to be equally divided among his five daughters. How many gold coins did the collector have in his collection?

'N OW CONSTABLE,' said the defendant's counsel in cross-examination. 'You say that the prisoner was exactly 27 steps ahead of you when you started to run after him?'

'Yes, sir.'

'And you swear that he takes eight steps to your five?'

'That is so.'

'Then I ask you, constable, as an intelligent man, to explain how you ever caught him if that is the case?'

'Well you see sir, I have got a longer stride. In fact, two of my steps are equal in length to five of the prisoner's. If you work it out, you will find that the number of steps I required would bring me exactly to the spot where I captured him.'

Here the foreman of the jury asked for a few minutes to work out the number of steps the constable must have taken. Can you also say how many steps the officer needed to catch the thief?

Q58   '2520'   A79

This is another puzzle devised by Boris Kordemsky about 1900.

SCHOLARS DISCOVERED '2520' in hieroglyphics engraved on a stone lid of a tomb in an Egyptian pyramid. Why was such an honour paid to this number?

Q59   THE AVERAGE SPEED PARADOX   A46

A CAR TRAVELS at a speed of 20 mph over a certain distance and then returns over the same distance at a speed of 30 mph. What is the average speed for the total journey?

Q60   NAPOLEON'S PROBLEM   A21

This puzzle is believed to have been proposed to Napoleon by the mathematician Loren Mascheroni, who was famous for his constructions.

1. Divide a circle with a known centre into four equal arcs using only a pair of compasses.
2. Rider: prove it.

The solution you are seeking was included by H.E. Dudeney in his 1926 book *Modern Puzzles.*

Q61   FILLING A BATH   A103

BATH PUZZLES appear in many forms, but this is a typical example.
You have accidentally left out the plug and are attempting to fill the bath with both taps full on. The hot tap takes 6 minutes to fill the bath, the cold tap takes 4 minutes, and the water empties through the plug hole in 12 minutes. In how many minutes will the bath be filled?

Magic squares are of great interest to us and we have a large
collection of them. They were developed by the Ancient Chinese
and consist of an array of numbers in which all rows, columns and
diagonals add up to the same total. Here are five examples,
each getting progressively more difficult.

1. This square is known as the
'Lo-shu', and, according to Chinese
legend, it is the first ever magic
square. It is said to have appeared
to the mythical Emperor Yü on the
back of a tortoise. Your task is to
re-create the square by inserting the
numbers from 1 to 9 once each only
so that each row, column and
corner-to-corner diagonal adds up to 15. There is only
one possible way in which this can be done, not counting rotations and reflections.

2. Insert the remaining numbers from 1 to 16 so that
each row, column and
corner-to-corner line adds
up to 34.

16			
			8
	12		
		4	

3. Insert the remaining
numbers from 1 to 25
so that each row,
column and corner-to-
corner line adds up
to 65.

		10		
				5
	25			
			20	
15				

4. Insert the remaining numbers from 1 to 36 so that each row, column and corner-to-corner line adds up to 111.

24			6		
		12			30
	18			36	

5. This is three magic squares in one. Insert the remaining numbers from 1 to 49 so that each row, column and corner-to-corner line adds up to 175. In addition, the middle 3 × 3 square will add up to 75, and the inner 5 × 5 square will add up to 125!

				49		
				35		
		21			14	7
		28				
		42				

– WORD PLAY –

WORD PUZZLES are probably the most popular and widely published of all puzzles, whether they be crosswords, anagrams, cryptograms or acrostics. Words are something with which everyone is familiar, for we all have to understand and speak the language to communicate, and the challenge of solving a word puzzle is one to which most of us like to respond.

We enjoy compiling puzzles as much as we enjoy solving them, and to try to illustrate our point we are presenting the following experiment, which we will call 'reverse anagrams' in which we invite you to be the compiler. We are listing a number of words, names or phrases and challenge you to come up with an appropriate anagram for each.

TELEVISION NEWS

FLORENCE NIGHTINGALE

GROVER CLEVELAND

LITTLE RED RIDING HOOD

LIKE A LAMB TO THE SLAUGHTER

PRESBYTERIAN

GOLDEN WEDDINGS

THE GOOD SAMARITANS

THE TOWERING INFERNO

When you think you have exhausted all the possibilities turn to A10, where you will find one anagram for each of the above, together with the name of the compiler where known. How many of you, we wonder, found the same anagram or something even more appropriate?

Crossword puzzles evolved from nineteenth-century puzzles called word forms, in which words are interlocked in geometric shapes. The first form published in America was a square, and appeared in a sporting paper *Wilkes' Spirit of the Times*, on 24 September 1859.

```
C I R C L E
I C A R U S
R A R E S T
C R E A T E
L U S T R E
E S T E E M
```

BY THE 1870s some puzzle constructors were producing what were termed double forms, in which different words read across and down. The following is in the shape of a diamond, and it was compiled by someone using the pseudonym Hyperion in *St Nicholas* Magazine of September 1875.

We have filled in the vowels, and you have to add the consonants to form words both across and down.

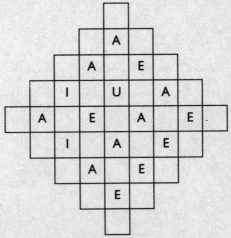

Here is a curiosity dating from the First World War when the
names listed below were on everybody's lips.

THERE IS NOTHING particularly unusual about the names
though – or is there?

KAISER
SERBIA
JOFFRE
FRENCH

This riddle is taken from Sam Loyd's *Cyclopedia of Puzzles*,
which was published in 1914.

In yon vast field of cultivated space,
I there am found with members of my race;
Decapitate me – if you've no objection –
You then will find what brings me to perfection;
Take one more cut, and then you'll plainly see,
What I am destined, day by day, to be.

THIS PUZZLE was compiled by the authors in 1987. We have compiled 160 cross-alphabet puzzles in which the object is to use each of the 26 letters of the alphabet once each only to form a crossword. The resulting grids come in all shapes and sizes, because they are determined by how the words can be fitted together as each different alphabet puzzle is built up. For many years we believed that the same grid could not possibly occur twice. That was until 1987, when we were able to produce the puzzle below in which we present you with two identical grids and a number of letters in identical positions in each. However, there the similarity ends. The puzzle is to insert in each grid the remaining letters of the alphabet so that each grid uses entirely different words and only the letters inserted have the same position in both grids. We believe that this is the first and only time that such a double-cross alphabet has been achieved.

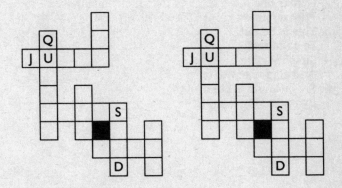

A N ACROSTIC is a composition in which the initial letters of the lines taken in order spell out a word or short sentence. Some are written as puzzles, while others make no attempt to conceal the answer. Sometimes the word is based on the last letter of a line (a telestitch), a combination of first and last letters (a double acrostic) or a more complex sequence.

The following is a rarely seen 'triple acrostic' in which the solution is based on the initial, middle and final letters of the answer words. The first couplet gives a clue to the answer as a whole and the five numbered couplets provide the five answer words. The acrostic is believed to date from around the middle of this century, but, alas, the author is unknown.

> Left, middle and right
> Give us a choice of light

1. The kind of glance which he who's lost his heart,
   Bestows on her who wears the latter part.
2. Here is one
   With a gun.
3. This is bound,
   To go round.
4. Simplify taste,
   And eliminate waste.
5. My meaning is plain,
   By my saying it again.

'Head-Heal-Teal-Tell-Tall-Tail'

THE ABOVE EXAMPLE was given by Lewis Carroll, the inventor of Doublets, when he wrote to the magazine *Vanity Fair* in March 1879 to describe the object of his new puzzle. Carroll had originally called the puzzle Word Links, the object being to find the shortest ladder between a given pair of words by changing one letter at a time. Carroll called the given words 'a doublet', the interposed words 'links' and the entire series 'a chain' Over the years his puzzle has remained popular and has also been called Laddergrams, Stepwords, Transitions, Transformation, Changelings, Passes, Word Chains, Word Ping-pong and Word Golf. In the following, the first 11 of which were compiled by Carroll, the number of links specified does not include the two doublets – for example, the head-to-tail puzzle above has four links. Recently computers have generated shorter solutions to many of Carroll's puzzles, but we are looking for Carroll's original solutions.

1. Nose to Chin in 5 links
2. Comb to Hair in 6 links
3. Four to Five in 6 links
4. Lion to Lamb in 2 links
5. Pity to Good in 6 links
6. Many to Fail in 7 links
7. Black to White in 5 links
8. Flour to Bread in 5 links
9. River to Shore in 10 links
10. Kettle to Holder in 9 links
11. Grass to Green in 7 links

Finally, in his 1925 *300 Best Word Puzzles,* H.E. Dudeney presents a number of word ladders of his own, of which the following is an example:

12. Kaiser to Porker in 10 links

This puzzle was compiled by one of the authors in 1986. It is by no means one of the most difficult of the puzzles we have compiled – in fact, it may be argued that it is one of the easiest. It is a simple substitution cryptogram in which each letter of the alphabet has been substituted for another. We have, however, included it in this collection because of the way in which the substitution has worked to produce an amusing tongue-twisting verse, which bears an uncanny resemblance to how the characters involved would have spoken it. Can you decode the verse?

'FLOP LOPY PLOP?' YOWS TWEE.
'PLU KEOP LOP,' YOWS TUG.
'IL, PLOP LOP,' YOWS TWEE.
'PLOPY PLOP PLUG.'

CAN YOU SOLVE the following riddle, which was devised by John Edward Field in 1871?

Come near, o men of wisdom, and search you through my ditty:

Four buried in this rubbish cities fair are lying low,

Search 'til on every line you see stand up a risen city.

'Till walls and arches, terraces and turrets, upward grow.

The following puzzle was compiled by one of the authors in 1985.

SOLVE THE CLUES that are hidden in the narrative and place the answers in the correct position in the grid.

'Pussy cat, pussy cat, from the Middle East, with long silky hair and a thick tail, where have you been?'

'I've been to the very middle part of London to see the Queen and Her royal sons, who accuse by legal processes, sets of co-ordinated doctrines.'

'Pussy cat, pussy cat, what did you do there?'

'I frightened some animals with strong incisors with a bend inwards, one of which is snugly embedded under a chair.'

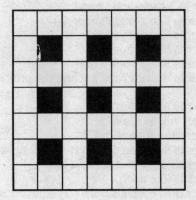

The following conundrums were all compiled between 1850 and 1920 and the answer given in each case is a different letter of the alphabet, but in no particular order. Most of these conundrums were researched by the American word expert A. Ross Eckler for his *Word Ways* Magazine of February 1991. Conundrums for the rare letters Q, X and Z are taken from Sam Loyd's 1914 *Cyclopedia of Puzzles.*

Example: What letter is like London?
Answer: E because it is the capital of England.

1. What letter is like an island?
2. What letter adds great value to a pear?
3. What letter has the same effect as thunder?
4. What letter is like a cow's tail?
5. What letter is like a schoolmaster?
6. What letter is like a selfish friend?
7. What letter comes once in a minute, twice in a moment and never in a thousand years?
8. What letter is like a scandalmonger?
9. What letter is like a mystery?
10. What letter is like a guide?
11. What letter is like a buck's tail?
12. What letter is the centre of joy and the principal mover of sorrow?
13. What letter is like death?
14. What letter widens a road?
15. What letter cannot be seen?
16. What letter is invisible yet never out of sight?
17. What letter changes the sex of a lad?
18. What letter is like noon?
19. What letter is like a pig's tail?
20. What letter is like the sun?
21. What letter is like a wedding ring?
22. What letter is the cleanest in the alphabet?
23. What letter is always the centre of mirth?
24. What letter is like the monkey cage?
25. What letter is always discovered in the centre of a maze?
26. What letter is like New Year's Day?

THROUGHOUT THE PAST one hundred years or so inventing anagrams has been a popular pastime. In the following all answers bear some relationship to the original. The name of the compiler and date of compilation is given, where known after each. An * indicates a capitalized name in the answer or part of the answer. The answer could be a name, just one word or a phrase.

1. *Genuine class (Dick Cavatt)
2. To scan a visible star or moon (V.E. Beckley)
3. I cry that I sin (Henry B. Wheatley, 1862)
4. No city dust here (Susan Eagleton, 1948)
5. Does ease thirst (David Schulman, 1936)
6. A rope ends it (H.H. Bailey, 1920)
7. Darn it! it is gone (William B. Kirk, 1911)
8. Docile, as a man tamed it (Mrs Bardwell, 1913)
9. Edge tools (E.J. McIlvane, 1907)
10. *Helps theology ('Awl Wrong', 1941)
11. *A thousand islets shine (Norman E. Nelson, 1925)
12. *Bold hearts fought in Kent ('Amaranth', 1901)
13. *English in flight, made port ('Viking', 1931)
14. Quit! I rob health (McCullough B. Wilson, 1915)
15. *Radium came (S. James Nesi, 1936)
16. *Gave us a damned clever satire (George W. Heywood, 1898)
17. Stop an ingress (D.C. Ver, 1898)
18. Reaps the blame for losing (Dr Arthur F. Klaycamp, 1908)
19. *Any labour I do wants time (H.E. Dudeney)
20. *Hasten on to fair Charlotte (Su San, 1934)

BOTH THESE RIDDLES were composed by the redoubtable Hubert Phillips. In each case you are looking for a one-word answer. Both riddles are very solvable.

1. My first wears my second; my third might be,
   What my first would acquire if he went to sea,
   Put together my one, two, three,
   And the belle of New York is the girl for me.

2. No hard decode, and, in this case,
   A solid answer you can claim.
   It has (I'm told) a different face,
   For every letter of its name.

AN ANTIGRAM is a re-arrangement of letters in a word or phrase into another word or phrase that is opposite in meaning. In the following you are looking for, in each case, an appropriate antigram. Where known, the name of the compiler and date of compilation are given in brackets. An * indicates a capitalized name.

1. A more mild act   (H. Grady Peerey, 1952)
2. Over fifty
3. Evil's agents   (Everett Ewing, 1927)
4. Arch saints   (Dr W.L. Sacrey, 1931)
5. Nice to imports   ('Hercules', 1928)
6. On the sly
7. Care is noted   (D.C. Ver, 1916)
8. Mad policy   ('Jemand', 1916)
9. *Gains power
10. I won't hear this   (James Lloyd Hood, 1964)

– MIGHTY BRAINBENDERS –

ALL PUZZLES are mighty brainbenders, especially if you cannot solve them. However, the ones we have chosen for this section are all, in our opinion, very difficult.

We think that one of the most difficult of all puzzles to comprehend is the Game of Logic, which was first published by Lewis Carroll in 1886. Originally intended for a childhood audience, it has since been conceded that most of these puzzles are 'university graduate standard'. The object is to deduce one single conclusion from all the statements given. The secret is to take from the series given any two statements with a common term and to draw a conclusion from them. The result is then combined with another premise from the series with a common term and another conclusion reached. You continue thus until only two statements remain, which then yield the ultimate conclusion.

Let us take, for example, one of Carroll's simpler examples:

1. No one takes in *The Times* unless he is well-educated.
2. No hedgehogs can read.
3. Those who cannot read are not well-educated.

Suppose we examine premises 1 and 3. We might conclude that no one who cannot read takes in *The Times*. Then, if you combine this conclusion with premise 2, you might conclude that 'No hedgehogs take in *The Times*', and this is exactly the solution that Carroll intended.

Now try the following, which was also compiled by Lewis Carroll. The answer is given as A22.

1. The only animals in this house are cats.
2. Every animal is suitable for a pet, that loves to gaze at the moon.
3. When I detest an animal, I avoid it.
4. No animals are carnivorous, unless they prowl at night.
5. No cat fails to kill mice.
6. No animals ever take to me, except that are in this house.
7. Kangaroos are not suitable for pets.
8. None but carnivora kill mice.
9. I detest animals that do not take to me.
10. Animals, that prowl at night, always love to gaze at the moon.

The following puzzle was originated by Nicholas Bernoulli
(1695–1726), who was one of the famous family of Swiss
mathematicians from Basle.

A CORRESPONDENT writes seven letters and addresses
seven envelopes, one for each letter. In how many
ways can all of the letters be placed in wrong envelopes?

Q77   THE ULTIMATE   A112
COUNTERFEIT COIN PUZZLE

We have seen several good counterfeit coin puzzles but this is,
we believe, the best and most complex of them all. It is a very
old puzzle and, unfortunately, the author is unknown.

I N A PILE OF 12 COINS there is a single counterfeit coin,
which can be detected only by its weight. Using a balance
scale, how can you identify the counterfeit coin in only three
operations and determine whether it is heavy or light?

Q78   THE KNIGHT'S DANCE   A77

This ancient puzzle from Europe was posed by Guarini Di Forli
and dates from 1512.

M AKE THE TWO white knights change places with the
two black knights in the least number of moves.
See Q3 for the explanation of the knight's move.

Leonardo of Pisa (c.1175–1250), otherwise known as Fibonacci, is famous for the series of numbers (0, 1, 1, 2, 3, 5, 8, 13, 21, 34, etc.) that bears his name. The puzzle that created this series – 'How many pairs of rabbits will be produced in a year, beginning with a single pair, if in every month each pair bears a new pair which becomes productive from the second month on?' – is propounded in his book on mathematics *Liber Abaci (Book of the Abacus)*. That work also contains the following puzzle, said to be put to Fibonacci in 1225 by the Emperor Frederick II, who had come to Pisa to test Fibonacci's reputation.

FIND A SQUARE that remains a square when it is decreased by 5 or increased by 5.

Between 1874 and 1891 Lewis Carroll compiled what are known as his pillow problems, later to be published in May 1893 as Part II of *Curiosa Mathematica*. The one we present here, the thirty-first of such problems, was compiled on 14 March 1889. Carroll would compile the problems while lying awake at night, then in the morning he would write down the answer, followed by the question and then the detailed solution. Just one warning about the puzzle that follows: don't expect the answer you are looking for to have nice round figures – Carroll worked out his answer to minute fractions of a second.

'ON 1 JULY at 8 a.m. by my watch, it was 4 minutes past 8 a.m. by my clock. I went to Greenwich and, when my watch said noon, the true GMT was 5 minutes past noon. That evening, when my watch said 6 o'clock, the clock said one minute to 6 p.m.

'On 30 July, at 9 a.m. by my watch, it was 3 minutes to 9 by my clock. At Greenwich, when my watch said 10 minutes past noon, the true GMT was 5 minutes past 12. That evening, when my watch said 7 p.m., the clock said 2 minutes to 7 p.m.

'My watch is only wound up for each journey and goes uniformly during any one day: the clock is always going, and goes uniformly. How am I to know when it is true noon on 31 July?'

Jonathan Swift (1667–1745) was an Anglo-Irish clergyman, poet and satirist whose masterpiece was *Gulliver's Travels* (1726). He was author of the following riddle.

By something form'd, I nothing am,
Yet ev'ry thing that you can name;
In no place have I ever been,
Yet ev'rywhere I may be seen;
In all things false, yet always true,
I'm still the same – but never new,
Lifeless, Life's perfect form I wear,
Can show a Nose, Eye, Tongue, or Ear;
Yet neither Smell, See, Taste, or Hear.
All Shapes and Features I can boast,
No Flesh, no Bones, no Blood – no Ghost:
All colours, without Paint, put on,
And change like the Camelon,
Swiftly I come and enter there.
Where not a chink lets in the Air:
Like thought I'm in a Moment gone,
Nor can I ever be alone:
All things on Earth I imitate,
Faster than Nature can create;
Sometimes imperial Robes I wear,
Anon in Beggar's Rags appear:
A Giant now, and strait an Elf.
I'm ev'ry one, but ne'er myself;
Ne'er said I mourn, ne'er glad rejoice,
I move my Lips, but want a Voice;
I ne'er was born, nor e'er can die,
Then prythee tell me what am I?

The following puzzle was devised by one of the authors, who obtained the idea for it from an earlier, much more complicated puzzle, involving palindromic numbers.

THE LOCAL TEAM used 16 players during the season. The total score for each of the 16 players for the season was a different palindromic prime. None of the players scored a total number that was a five-digit prime, and all of them except one scored three 4s at least, except one player who scored two 4s and his total was of only two digits. When the 16 players' totals are added and then divided by 16 to reach an average, the average is a three-figure number, which consists of the same digit repeated three times.

What was the average?

Note: A palindromic number is one that reads the same backwards or forwards. A prime number is one which is greater than 1, which has no factors other than 1 and itself. An example of a palindromic prime number is 181.

This puzzle appears in an old Chinese book *Sonshi Sankyo* (Mathematical Bible of Military Science) and in several Japanese books on mathematics written between the sixteenth and nineteenth centuries.

YOU OFFER TO GUESS someone's age and take them through the following stages:

1. Ask them to divide their age by 3 and tell you the remainder. Say, for example, it is 2.
2. Ask them to divide their age by 5 and tell you the remainder. Say for example, it is 1
3. Ask them to divide their age by 7 and tell you the remainder. Say, for example, it is 6.

From this information you correctly calculate that their age is 41. How is this done?

This puzzle was devised by one of the authors who remembered seeing the 'roll-a-penny' game at fairgrounds many years ago.

WE ALL REMEMBER the old fairground game, which is still to be found, where the object is to roll a coin down a chute to land in a square without touching a line to win the prize in the square in which it has landed.

How does one calculate the chances of winning?

Below is an example of a typical linoleum-topped barker's table on which the game is played. What are the odds against the punter winning?

The coin is 1 inch in diameter and the squares are 2 × 2 inches.

Repeating pattern

4	4	4	4
4	6	8	4
4	8	10	4
4	4	4	4

2in

1in ○

The following puzzle was originated by the English scholar Alcuin, who spent his life at the court of Charlemagne.

A KING ORDERED his servant to collect an army from 30 manors in such a way that from each manor he would take the same number of men as he had collected up to then. The servant went to the first manor alone, the second he went with one other.

How many men were collected in all?

IT WAS IN 1848 that a certain Max Bezzel proposed what is now known as the problem of the eight queens when he asked: 'What is the largest number of queens that can be placed on an 8 × 8 chess board in such a way that no queen is attacked by another? As anyone with a basic knowledge of chess will immediately deduce, this means that no two queens must be in the same row, column or diagonal because, of course, the queen, being the most powerful piece in the game of chess, can move any distance in any direction in a straight line as shown in the diagram.

Although it was soon determined how many pieces were necessary, it was not until 1850 that the total number of possible solutions (not counting rotations and reflections of the same solution) was published, and not until 1874 that the proof was published by the English mathematician J.W.L. Glaisher.

Can you determine the following?

1. The largest number of queens that can be placed.
2. The number of possible different solutions.

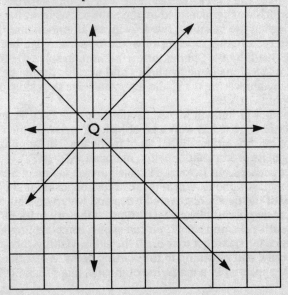

– CLASSIC KICKSELF –

A stick I found that weighed two pound:
 I sewed it up one day
In pieces of eight of equal weight!
 How much did each piece weigh?
Lewis Carroll

THE TERM 'kickself puzzle' was said to have been coined at a Mensa dinner in Cambridge some years ago when science fiction writer Arthur C. Clarke asked inventor Sir Clive Sinclair: 'What was the first human artefact to break the sound barrier?' There was a brief pause before Clive Sinclair gave the correct answer. (A33)

However, as can be seen from the rhyme above, kickself-type puzzles – those where you kick yourself when you hear the answer – have been around for many years. The question posed above by Lewis Carroll looks to be the simplest mathematical question imaginable, a simple matter of dividing two by eight, but as might be expected it is not quite that simple, as you will see if you turn to A11.

Perhaps the first kickself puzzle was the one in Greek legend which was propounded by the Sphinx: 'What walks on four legs in the morning, two legs in the afternoon and three legs in the evening?' Scores of would-be solvers had been put to death by the Sphinx for their failure to solve the riddle until Oedipus came to Thebes and won his throne by correctly answering the riddle. Can you solve the riddle of the Sphinx? (A29)

Another prominent Mensa member, the late Isaac Asimov, also once weighed in with a great kickself puzzle, which is one of our favourites: 'What word in the English language changes its pronunciation when nationalized?' (A72)

But perhaps our favourite kickself puzzle is one of Sam Loyd's most famous, which is illustrated opposite. It shows a map of the newly discovered cities and waterways on our nearest neighbour planet, Mars. Start at the city marked T, at the South Pole, and see if you can spell a complete English sentence by making a tour of all the cities, visiting each city once only, and returning to the starting point. When the puzzle appeared in a magazine originally, more than 50,000 readers reported, 'there is no possible way,' and yet it is a very simple puzzle. Why was that? (A47)

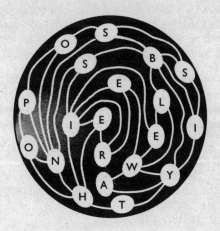

A MAN HAS 100 YARDS of cloth in a single roll, and he wishes to divide it into 100 lengths of 1 yard each. It takes him 3 seconds to cut each length. Working flat-out, non-stop, how long does it take him to cut all 100 pieces?

Sometimes a chap'll
  Find, in some trivial happening, inspiration:
The fall of an apple
Led – so 'tis said, a Cambridge don to grapple
  With the mysteries of the Laws of Gravitation.
The Royal Society
Remembers him with piety.

THE ABOVE was penned by Hubert Phillips for his quiz book *Tell Me Who*, described as 'a biographical puzzle game'. The answer, of course, is Sir Isaac Newton (1642–1727), who was president of the Royal Society and composer of the following riddle.

Four people sat down at a table to play;
They played all that night, and some part of next day;
This one thing observed, that when all were seated,
Nobody played with them, and nobody betted:
Yet, when they got up, each was winner a guinea;
Who tells me this riddle, I'm sure is no ninny.

Incidentally, we would have loved to have listened to the dialect of Isaac Newton to learn how he managed to get 'seated' to rhyme with 'betted'.

Here is another puzzle by Boris Kordemsky, dating from c.1900.

Find a simple method of solving:

6751X	+	3249Y	=	26751
3249X	+	6751Y	=	23249

This puzzle was compiled by one of the authors in 1986, and it illustrates how suddenly ideas for puzzles can hit you. The idea came after he had finished work for the day and was relaxing watching the Dave Allen show on television. The comedian started telling a joke about a lift going up and down in a department store and the puzzle idea flashed through his head. He dashed upstairs to his study and committed the following puzzle to paper. He never did hear the end of the joke!

I WAS ON the second floor of a New York department store recently. 'Let's take the lift,' said my wife. 'It won't be long; it's on the third floor and coming down'. We waited, but to our annoyance it shot straight past us to floor one, then up to the fourth floor, straight back down to the first again and then back up to the fifth. 'This is useless,' I said. 'Let's walk.' 'No, hang on for a few more minutes,' said my wife. 'It will probably continue straight up to the ninth floor and then come straight back down to us.' We waited, and sure enough the lift did exactly as my wife had predicted. How did she know?

Here is a clever kickself puzzle by H.E. Dudeney.

A BALL 13 INCHES in diameter has a 5-inch hole drilled through the centre. How deep is the hole?

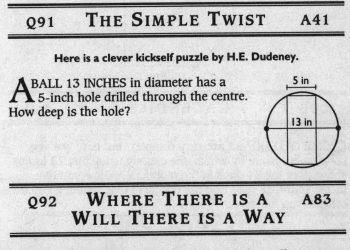

A N OLD LADY left £33,333 to be divided equally among two fathers and two sons and each was to receive £11,111. How was this possible?

SOMETHING IN COMMON

This puzzle was compiled by one of the authors in 1990.

WHAT HAVE the following in common?

A MINE
A HOLM OAK
A HUT

Q94 AN ANGLE ON A CUBE A105

AB AND BC are two diagonals drawn on the face of a cube. How many degrees is the angle created at ABC?

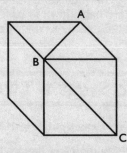

Q95   CALENDICE   A91

SOME CALENDARS are very complex, but here is a very simple system by which one can, by using just 12 faces, show all of the 31 days in the month. We show you five faces. Your task is to find the numbers that should go on the other seven faces.

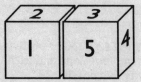

The following conundrum was posed by the English Whig
statesman Charles James Fox (1749–1806).

I WENT TO THE CRIMEA; I stopped there, and I never went
there, and I came back again. What am I?

Here is another of Sam Loyd's kickselfs.

WHILE ENJOYING a giddy ride on the carousel Sammy
proposed this problem.
  One-third of the number of kids riding ahead of me,
added to three-quarters of those riding behind me, gives the
correct number of children on this merry-go-round.
  How many children were riding on the carousel?

– PERPLEXITIES –

AMAN IS LOOKING at a portrait and he says: 'Sisters and brothers have I none, but that man's father is my father's son.'

Hubert Phillips once remarked that he had received scores of letters asking him to settle arguments as to whose portrait the man was looking at. Phillip's reaction to this was to comment as follows:

'I think it is pathetic that having sufficient interest in abstractions to tackle the problem, my correspondents have not sufficient confidence in their own powers of reasoning to satisfy themselves as to the answer. The only possible explanation is that their capacity to use their wits has fallen into disuse. I have often heard the above "chestnut" hotly debated – and by quite intelligent people too. "It's himself" – "It's his son." "It's his grandson." Yet how few of those participating in such arguments will adopt the obvious line of approach:

'You say it's himself. In that case "that man's father" – i.e., the speaker's father is also the speaker's father's son. Does that make sense? Or can a man be his own father? And *you* say, madam, "It's his grandson". Let us test *your* hypothesis. "That man's father" now becomes the speaker's grandson's father – in other words, the speaker's son. Thus the speaker's son is also the speaker's father's son – i.e., the speaker himself. Does *that* make sense? And now the answer should be apparent – that the portrait is that of the speaker's son.'

Notwithstanding Hubert Phillips' tongue in cheek comments, it is still today a conundrum that catches out many people, and maybe, if you were not confused at the outset, you will be after reading Mr Phillips' explanation of how to solve the puzzle.

More perplexities follow in this section.

CONFUSION AT THE RECTORY

The following puzzle was compiled by Hubert Phillips.

THE RECTOR'S FOUR BOYS have done their best to make the dog situation at the rectory confusing. Each of the four – their names are Alec, Bob, Charlie and David – owns two dogs, and each has named his dogs after two of his brothers. Each boy has, in consequence, two doggy namesakes.

Of the eight dogs, three are cocker spaniels, three are terriers and two are dachshunds. None of the four boys owns two dogs of the same breed. No two dogs of the same breed have the same name. Neither of Alec's dogs is named David and neither of Charlie's dogs is named Alec. No cocker spaniel is named Alec, and no terrier is named David. Bob does not own a terrier.

Who are the owners and what are the names of the dachshunds?

THE VILLAGE SIMPLETON

Here is another puzzle from H.E. Dudeney

A FACETIOUS INDIVIDUAL, who was taking a long walk in the country, came upon a yokel sitting on a stile. As the gentleman was not quite sure of his road, he thought he would make enquiries of the local inhabitant; but at the first glance he jumped too hastily to the conclusion that he had dropped on the village idiot. He, therefore, decided to test the fellow's intelligence first by putting to him the simplest question he could think of, which was: 'What day of the week is this, my good man?' The following is the smart answer that he received:

'When the day after tomorrow is yesterday, today will be as far from Sunday as today was from Sunday when the day before yesterday was tomorrow.'

Can you say what day of the week it was? It is pretty evident that the countryman was not such a fool as he looked. The gentleman went on the road a puzzled but a wiser man.

THE
GET OFF THE EARTH
PUZZLE

Sam Loyd designed the above puzzle in 1896 as an advertisement for Bergen Beach, a newly opened resort in New Jersey, and he regarded it as his greatest puzzle.

THE PUZZLE consists of two concentric pieces of cardboard, fastened together so that the smaller, inner circle pivots backwards and forwards. In the left-hand illustration there are 13 Chinese warriors, but in the right-hand illustration, after the wheel has been turned slightly there are only 12. The puzzle has generated a great deal of speculation over the years and several explanations have been put forward, including Loyd's 'red herring' that he changed a right leg for a left leg between the fourth and fifth man.

What is the explanation?

PATIENCE

There are several legends concerning the origin of this famous puzzle, which was the invention of Edouard Lucas and was sold as a toy in France in 1883. Lucas's version has it that in the great temple of Benares are 64 golden discs of different sizes and mounted on three pillars, two of diamond and one of gold. When

he created the universe, the God Brahma placed all 64 discs on one of the diamond pegs in descending order of size, with the largest disc at the bottom. The temple priests had to transfer the discs from one pillar to another. However, a larger disc was never allowed to be placed on top of a smaller disc. As soon as all 64 discs had been transferred to the gold pillar the universe would end. Fortunately for us all, if the priests transferred a disc every second of every day it would take them many millions of years to complete their task. The actual mathematics of the task are that the number of moves required for a given number of discs is $2^n - 1$. Thus 3 discs could be transferred in 7 moves, 5 discs in 31 moves and 16 discs in 65535 moves, etc.

THE CARD GAME below is an adaptation of this old puzzle and nine cards of the same suit are used, from 2 to 10 inclusive. They are laid out in three rows of three as shown. The object is to get the cards to a single column in descending sequence by moving according to the following rules:

1. One card only may be moved at a time.
2. It must be a card from the foot of a column.
3. It can be placed only at the foot of another column and only below a higher card.

When a 'vacancy' occurs – i.e., when all the cards in one column have been moved – the bottom card of either of the remaining columns may be used to fill the vacancy.

Virgil was the sobriquet of Publius Vergilius Maro (70–19 BC).
He was the supreme poet of Imperial Rome and the object of
superstitious reverence to later generations. He compiled
the following riddle.

DAMOETAS: Read me this riddle and I shall take you for
Apollo's self. 'Where in the world is the sky no more
than three yards wide?'

JIM IS 36 years old. He is twice as old as Sid was when he,
Jim, was as old as Sid is now. How old was Sid a year
ago?

THE FOLLOWING PUZZLE was devised by one of the
authors, who adapted it from an earlier, almost impossible puzzle, based on square and cube numbers. This one is
much more soluble.

A has thought of a number between 13 and 1300.
B is trying to guess it.
B asks whether the number is below 500.
A says yes.
B asks if the number is a perfect cube.
A says yes.
B asks if the number is a perfect square.
A says yes.
A says that only two of his answers are correct and the
    number starts with 5, 7 or 9.
B now knows the number.

What is it?

THE TANGRAM PUZZLE is probably the most ancient in origin of all dissection puzzles. It is believed to have originated in China 4000 years ago, although the earliest known reference to it is a wood-cut from 1780 by Utamoro, which depicts two courtesans trying to solve Chi-Chiao (the Seven Clever Pieces).

The puzzle is made up from seven pieces cut from a square as shown below and the object is to create tangram shapes from the seven pieces.

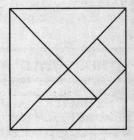

Lewis Carroll was, not surprisingly, fascinated by tangrams and owned a book, *The Fashionable Chinese Puzzle,* which contained 323 tangrams and which, on Carroll's death, passed to H.E. Dudeney. It was Dudeney who created the following paradox in which he illustrates two Chinamen, apparently identical except for the missing foot on the right-hand figure. However, both figures contain all seven identical tangram pieces. Can you create the two figures with the seven tangram pieces?

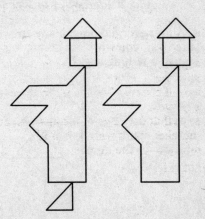

The Two Chinamen

'ERNIE' is a random number producer. Pi could also be said to be a random number producer, because the decimal equivalent is known to only 20 million places – nobody knows the hundredth-million or million-millionth decimal place. The most unusual feature of an infinite random number is that, for instance, 999999999 must occur somewhere within it, as in fact, must every possible combination of digits that you wish to name. So, if you had a random number sequence, what would be the average difference between two random digits side by side?

Strangely enough it is not

$$\frac{0+9}{2} = 4\frac{1}{2}$$

'THE HATTER opened his eyes very wide on hearing this; but all he said was, "Why is a raven like a writing desk?" "Come, we shall have some fun now!" thought Alice. "I'm glad they've begun asking riddles – I believe I can guess that" she added aloud.'

Alice's Adventures in Wonderland, Lewis Carroll

But, Alice never did provide the answer and neither did the Hatter. Can you work out an answer to the riddle:'Why is a raven like a writing desk?'

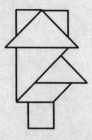

Mad Hatter Tangram (H.E. Dudeney)

CAN YOU DECODE the following message which was sent, undetected, in 1862 during the American Civil War? Who sent the message?

Burnside, Acquia Creek:

Can Inn Ale me withe 2 oar our Ann pas Ann me flesh ends N.V. Corn Inn out with U cud Inn heaven day nest Wed Roe Moor Tom darkey hat Creek Why Hawk of abbot Inn b chewed I if - Bates.

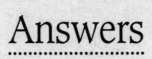

Answers

– ANSWERS –

A1   Squaring the Urn   Q43

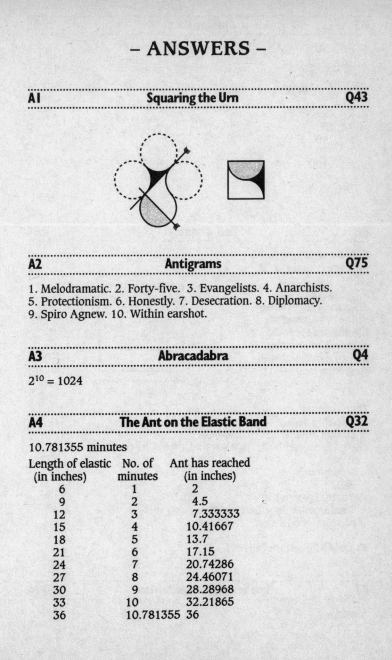

A2   Antigrams   Q75

1. Melodramatic. 2. Forty-five. 3. Evangelists. 4. Anarchists.
5. Protectionism. 6. Honestly. 7. Desecration. 8. Diplomacy.
9. Spiro Agnew. 10. Within earshot.

A3   Abracadabra   Q4

$2^{10} = 1024$

A4   The Ant on the Elastic Band   Q32

10.781355 minutes

Length of elastic (in inches)	No. of minutes	Ant has reached (in inches)
6	1	2
9	2	4.5
12	3	7.333333
15	4	10.41667
18	5	13.7
21	6	17.15
24	7	20.74286
27	8	24.46071
30	9	28.28968
33	10	32.21865
36	10.781355	36

```
1. 135) 2970 (22
        270
        270
        270
```

```
2. 13) 8290 (637
       78
       49
       39
      100
       91
        9
```

In order to win, the punter's coin must fall within the shaded area shown in the diagram. If the centre of the coin is outside the shaded area, the coin will be covering part of a line and will, therefore, be a loser.

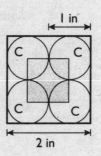

Therefore:

Winning area	=	1 sq in
Losing area	=	3 sq in

The odds should be 3:1 against and should pay out:

Win	6
Money back	2
Total	8

The actual pay out is:

Total number in squares = $\frac{80}{16}$ = 5 pay out
Number of squares = 16

The odds favour the barker 8 : 5.

A watch

Train to 15-metre siding; collect coach B. Back to 15-metre siding; leave B in 5-metre siding. Back to 15-metre siding; up to top; pick up A and push down on to B in 5-metre siding. Reverse up to top. Drop B in its original place and come back with A to the top. Take A to 5-metre siding and leave. Reverse to top; collect B and reverse to top. Leave B in A's original position. Reverse train and go across to 15-metre siding. Push A up to B's original position and return train to starting point.

At present the hole is 3ft 6in deep and the man is 2ft 4in above ground. When it is complete, the hole will be 10ft 6in deep and the man will be 4ft 8in below the surface.

Its now seen live	(James I. Rambo)
Flit on cheering angel	(Lewis Carroll)
Govern, clever lad	(Dmitiri Borgmann)
The door ring tided ill	
Kill bleaters, ah! tough meat	(Carter/Russell)
Best in prayer	
Sign long wedded	
Hearts go to man's aid	(Loris B. Curtis)
One fire went right on	(Jeane E. Roman)

In Shylock's bargain for the flesh was found
  No mention of the blood that flowed around:
So when that stick sewed in pieces eight,
  The sawdust lost diminished from the weight.

Lewis Carroll

Sunday

1:1	0	2:2	3:4	■	4:9	■	5:8	6:6	4	7:9
3	■	8:5	4	9:3	1	10:4	9	9	■	2
11:3	12:6	■	13:5	4	2	8	9	■	14:1	6
15:1	6	16:9	■	17:3	2	4	■	18:1	1	1
■	19:4	7	20:7		5	■	21:1	2	1	
22:4	3	2	4	5	■	23:1	1	2	1	24:7
■	25:6	2	5	■	26:1	■	27:4	2	1	■
28:6	2	5	■	29:3	2	30:1	■	31:2	1	32:0
33:5	3	■	34:7	3	3	3	35:2	■	36:1	3
6	■	37:4	2	8	2	6	1	38:6	■	9
39:1	2	9	6	■	40:1	■	41:6	4	9	8

A14 The Capital and Labour Puzzle Q29

Number the men from 1 to 6, starting at the top. The sequence is then:
1. 1 takes over 2 and returns with the boat.
2. 1 takes over 3 and returns with the boat.
3. 4 and 5 go over, and 4 brings back 2.
4. 4 takes 1 over and brings back 3.
5. 4 and 6 go over, and 1 brings back the boat.
6. 1 takes over 2 and brings back the boat.
7. 1 takes over 3.

A15 Confusion at the Rectory Q98

The dachshunds are Alec (owned by Bob) and David (owned by Charlie).

A16   Probability   Q15

1. $20/50 \times 30/49 = 600/2450 = 1850$ to 600
2. $30/50 \times 20/49 = 600/2450 = 1850$ to 600
3. $20/50 \times 19/49 = 380/2450 = 2070$ to 380
4. $30/50 \times 29/49 = 870/2450 = 1580$ to 870

A17   Schiller's Riddle   Q7

The Great Wall of China

A18   Circles   Q33

Both circles are the same size.

A19   The Urban Riddle   Q70

Four towns can be found, one on each line: Rome, Ely, Paris, Chester.

A20   Roll of Cloth   Q87

This is similar to the classic question: 'How long does it take a clock to strike 12 if there is a 1 second between strikes?' In that case, the answer is 11 seconds, because the first two strikes take only 1 second. When it comes to the roll of cloth, the answer is not, as some may suppose, $100 \times 3 = 300$ seconds. This is incorrect because the 100 pieces are obtained with 99 cuts, the first two pieces coming with a single cut. The answer is, therefore, $99 \times 3 = 297$ seconds.

A21   Napoleon's Problem   Q60

1. Choose any point, A, on the circle, and with radius O-A and centres A, B and C, mark B, C and D. With radius A-C and centres A and D, draw arcs intersecting at E. With radius O-E and centre A, draw the arc cutting the circle at F and G. A, F, D and G are the required points defining the arcs, being the corners of an inscribed square. Although this is elegantly done with six arcs, a five-arc solution is also possible.

2. Assume a unit radius – i.e., O-D = 1.

AB = BC = CD, therefore, <COD = 60°
therefore, CD = OD = 1
<ACD = 90°
therefore, AC = √3 = AE
<AOE = 90°
therefore, OE = √2 = AF
similarly, FD = √2 and <AFD = 90°
similarly, AG = GD = √2 and <AGD = 90°

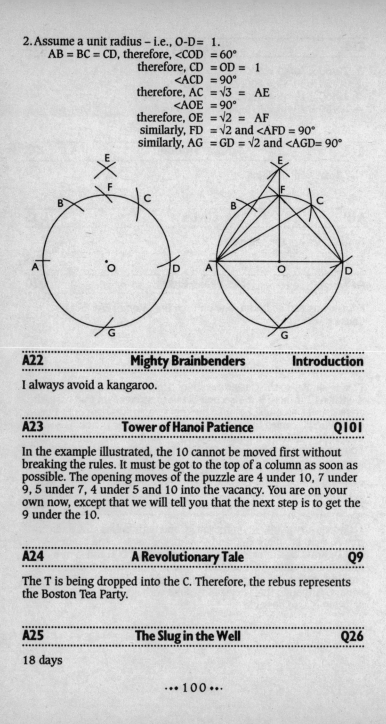

I always avoid a kangaroo.

A23   **Tower of Hanoi Patience**   **Q101**

In the example illustrated, the 10 cannot be moved first without breaking the rules. It must be got to the top of a column as soon as possible. The opening moves of the puzzle are 4 under 10, 7 under 9, 5 under 7, 4 under 5 and 10 into the vacancy. You are on your own now, except that we will tell you that the next step is to get the 9 under the 10.

A24   **A Revolutionary Tale**   **Q9**

The T is being dropped into the C. Therefore, the rebus represents the Boston Tea Party.

A25   **The Slug in the Well**   **Q26**
---

18 days

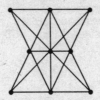

A27   **Carpenter**   **Q48**

He worked on 18 days and did not work on 12 days.

A28   **Triple Acrostic**   **Q67**

A do	R in	G
M usk	E tee	R
B an	D ag	R
E con	O miz	E
R eite	R atio	N

A29   **Classic Kickself**   **Introduction**

It is man, who crawls on all fours as a child, walks on two legs as an adult and walks with the aid of a stick in old age.

A30   **Tangrams**   **Q105**

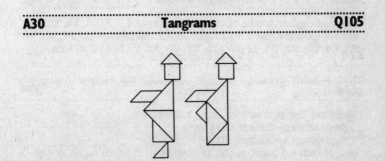

Let the men be A, B, and C and let the wives be a, b and c.

Bank	Boat	Opposite bank
ACac	Bb	None
ACac	B	b
ABC	ac	b
ABC	a	bc
Aa	BC	bc
Aa	Bb	Cc
ab	AB	Cc
ab	c	ABC
b	ac	ABC
b	B	ACac
None	Bb	ACac

The constable took 30 steps. In the same time the thief would take 48, which, added to his start of 27, would have carried him 75 steps. The distance would be exactly equal to 30 steps of the constable.

The whip

At the bottom of a well

The first capture can be of any pawn except C4, D3, D4, E5, E6 or F5. For example, place the knight on A3 and capture C2, B4, D3, B2, C4, D2, B3, D4, E6, G7, F5, E7, G6, E5, F7 and G5 in turn.

There are 2 men, 5 women and 13 children
   men+women+children=20 people
   men+women+children=20 coins
(no. of men × 3 coins) = (no. of women × 1½ coins) = (no. of children × ½ coin) = (2 × 3) + (5 × 1½) + (13 × ½) = 20 coins

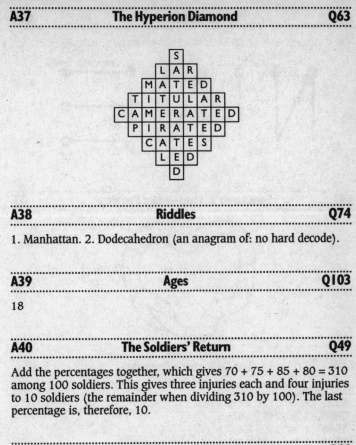

1. Manhattan. 2. Dodecahedron (an anagram of: no hard decode).

18

Add the percentages together, which gives $70 + 75 + 85 + 80 = 310$ among 100 soldiers. This gives three injuries each and four injuries to 10 soldiers (the remainder when dividing 310 by 100). The last percentage is, therefore, 10.

12 inches. Our old friend Pythagoras solves this one:
$13^2 = 12^2 + 5^2$.

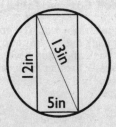

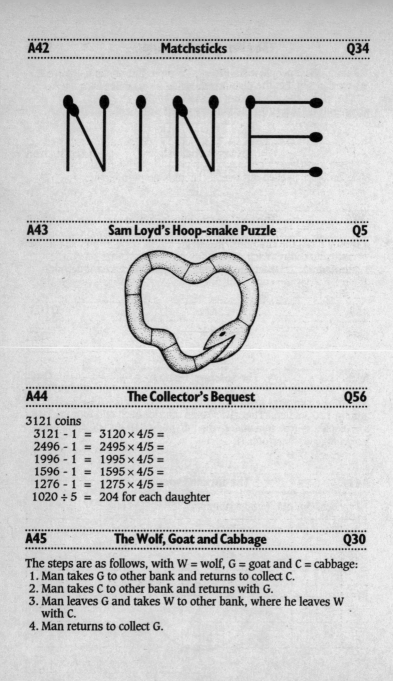

A43   Sam Loyd's Hoop-snake Puzzle   Q5

A44   The Collector's Bequest   Q56

3121 coins

$$3121 - 1 = 3120 \times 4/5 =$$
$$2496 - 1 = 2495 \times 4/5 =$$
$$1996 - 1 = 1995 \times 4/5 =$$
$$1596 - 1 = 1595 \times 4/5 =$$
$$1276 - 1 = 1275 \times 4/5 =$$
$$1020 \div 5 = 204 \text{ for each daughter}$$

A45   The Wolf, Goat and Cabbage   Q30

The steps are as follows, with W = wolf, G = goat and C = cabbage:
 1. Man takes G to other bank and returns to collect C.
 2. Man takes C to other bank and returns with G.
 3. Man leaves G and takes W to other bank, where he leaves W
    with C.
 4. Man returns to collect G.

24 mph. Most people instantly say 25 mph, but this is not correct, as we can see. Let the distance travelled be 60 miles each way.
   Therefore, the journey out = $^{60}/_{20}$ = 3 hours
   Therefore, the 120-mile journey = $^{120}/_5$ = 24 mph

A47 .... **Classic Kickself** .... **Introduction**

The sentence spelled out reads: 'There is no possible way.'

A48 .... **The Get Off the Earth Puzzle** **Q100**

As they cross the circumference of the circle, the warriors spiral towards its centre. Each man sends forwards a larger section of some part of him than he receives, and thus produces an accumulated figure at the end of the line - i.e., the 13 warriors merge into 12 slightly larger warriors.

A49 .... **Magic Squares** **Q62**

1.

8	1	6
3	5	7
4	9	2

2.

16	6	11	1
9	3	14	8
2	12	5	15
7	13	4	10

3.

23	4	10	11	17
6	12	18	24	5
9	25	1	7	13
2	8	14	20	21
15	16	22	3	9

4.

24	19	26	6	1	35
25	23	21	7	32	3
20	27	22	2	9	31
15	10	17	33	28	8
16	14	12	34	5	30
11	18	13	29	36	4

5.

4	9	8	47	48	49	10
38	19	20	17	34	35	12
39	37	26	27	22	13	11
43	36	21	25	29	14	7
6	18	28	23	24	32	44
5	15	30	33	16	31	45
40	41	42	3	2	1	46

Musicians

A52   **Doublets**   **Q68**

1. Nose-note-cote-core-corn-coin-chin. 2. Comb-come-home-hole-hale-hall-hail-hair. 3. Four-foul-fool-foot-fort-fore-fire-five.
4. Lion-limn-limb-lamb. 5. Pity-pits-pins-fins-find-fond-food-good.
6. Many-mane-wane-wale-wile-will-wall-wail-fail. 7. Black-blank-blink-clink-chink-chine-whine-white. 8. Flour-floor-flood-blood-brood-broad-bread. 9. River-rover-cover-coves-cores-corns-coins-chins-shins-shine-shone-shore. 10. Kettle-settle-settee-setter-better-betted-belted-bolted-bolter-bolder-holder.
11. Grass-crass-cress-tress-trees-frees-freed-greed-green.
12. Kaiser-raiser-raised-railed-failed-foiled-coiled-cooled-cooked-corked-corker-porker.

A53   **Couriers**   **Q17**

The speeds of the couriers are $^{250}/_7$ and $^{250}/_9$, so their approach speed was:

$$250 \left(\tfrac{1}{7} + \tfrac{1}{9} \right) = 250 \times {}^{16}/_{63}$$

and they will meet in

$$^{63}/_{16} = 3^{15}/_{16} \text{ days}$$

A54   **The Famous Farmer's Horses Puzzle**   **Q25**

One-half, one-quarter and one-fifth do not add up to unity - i.e.,
$0.5 + 0.25 + 0.2 = 0.95$.

41, 80, 320

A reflection in a mirror.

3.3
Difference
↓

0 – 0	0	1 – 0	1	2 – 0	2	3 – 0	3	4 – 0	4	5 – 0	5
0 – 1	1	1 – 1	0	2 – 1	1	3 – 1	2	4 – 1	3	5 – 1	4
0 – 2	2	1 – 2	1	2 – 2	0	3 – 2	1	4 – 2	2	5 – 2	3
0 – 3	3	1 – 3	2	2 – 3	1	3 – 3	0	4 – 3	1	5 – 3	2
0 – 4	4	1 – 4	3	2 – 4	2	3 – 4	2	4 – 4	1	5 – 4	1
0 – 5	5	1 – 5	4	2 – 5	3	3 – 5	3	4 – 5	2	5 – 5	0
0 – 6	6	1 – 6	5	2 – 6	4	3 – 6	4	4 – 6	3	5 – 6	1
0 – 7	7	1 – 7	6	2 – 7	5	3 – 7	5	4 – 7	4	5 – 7	2
0 – 8	8	1 – 8	7	2 – 8	6	3 – 8	6	4 – 8	5	5 – 8	3
0 – 9	9	1 – 9	8	2 – 9	7	3 – 9	7	4 – 9	6	5 – 9	4
	45		37		31		27		25		25

6 – 0	6	7 – 0	7	8 – 0	8	9 – 0	9	45
6 – 1	5	7 – 1	6	8 – 1	7	9 – 1	8	37
6 – 2	4	7 – 2	5	8 – 2	6	9 – 2	7	31
6 – 3	3	7 – 3	4	8 – 3	5	9 – 3	6	27
6 – 4	2	7 – 4	3	8 – 4	4	9 – 4	5	25
6 – 5	1	7 – 5	2	8 – 5	3	9 – 5	4	25
6 – 6	0	7 – 6	1	8 – 6	2	9 – 6	3	27
6 – 7	1	7 – 7	0	8 – 7	1	9 – 7	2	31
6 – 8	2	7 – 8	1	8 – 8	0	9 – 8	1	37
6 – 9	3	7 – 9	2	8 – 9	1	9 – 9	0	45
	27		31		37		45	330

$330 \div 100 = 3.3$

Add the equations to give
$$10000x + 10000y = 50000$$
Divide by 10000 to give
$$x + y = 5$$
Subtract to give
$$3502x - 3502y = 3502$$
Divide by 3502 to give
$$x - y = 1$$
Therefore, $x = 3$, $y = 2$

A59   Beheadments   Q65

Wheat, heat, eat

A60   Visual Deceptions   Q39

1. They are both the same. 2. B. 3. A

A61   How Old is Mary?   Q51

Mary is 27½ years old.

A62   Letter Conundrums   Q72

1. T is in the middle of water. 2. L makes a pear into a pearl. 3. S makes our cream sour cream. 4. F comes at the end of beef. 5. C forms lasses into classes. 6. P is the first in pity and the last in help. 7. M. 8. W makes ill will. 9. X is inexplicable. 10. Q goes ahead of U (you). 11. N is at the end of venison. 12. O. 13. E is at the end of life. 14. B makes it broad. 15. V is invisible. 16. I. 17. Y changes lad to lady. 18. A is in the middle of day. 19. K is at the end of pork. 20. G is in the centre of light. 21. D because we could not be wed without it. 22. H because it is in the middle of washing. 23. U is in the middle of fun. 24. Z is the leading feature of the zoo. 25. R is in the middle of labyrinth. 26. J is the first of January.

A63   Jigsaw Puzzles   Q3

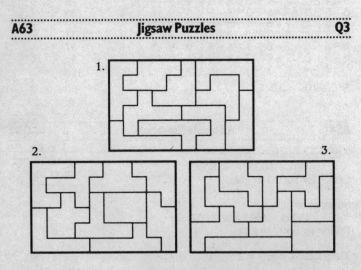

Place Nos. 1 and 2 close together, as in Fig. 1; then hold them together with the finger and thumb of the left hand horizontally and with the square hole to the right. Push No.3 – placed in the same position *facing you* (a) in No.4 – through the opening at K, and slide it to the left at A, so that the profile of the pieces should be as in Fig. 2.

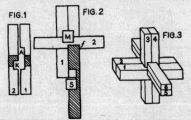

Now push No.4 *partially* through the space from below upwards, as seen in f Fig. 2. Place No.5 cross ways upon the part Y, so that the point 2 is directed upwards to the right hand side; then push No.4 quite through, and it will be in the position shown by the dotted lines in Fig. 2. All that now remains is to push No.6 – which is the key – through the opening M and the cross is completed as in Fig. 3.

56

KAI	SER
SER	BIA
JOF	FRE
FRE	NCH

Although it is not a particularly sophisticated code, it was, never-theless, not deciphered. What is necessary is to start at the end and continue to the beginning, paying attention to the sounds of the words. Note that the word 'flesh' was, in those days, commonly used instead of the word 'meat'. The message read:

Major-General Burnside, Acquia Creek, Va.
If I should be in boat off Acquia Creek at dark tomorrow,
Wednesday evening, could you without inconvenience, meet
[flesh] me and pass an hour or two with me.   A. Lincoln

7 + 49 + 343 + 2401 + 16807 = 19607

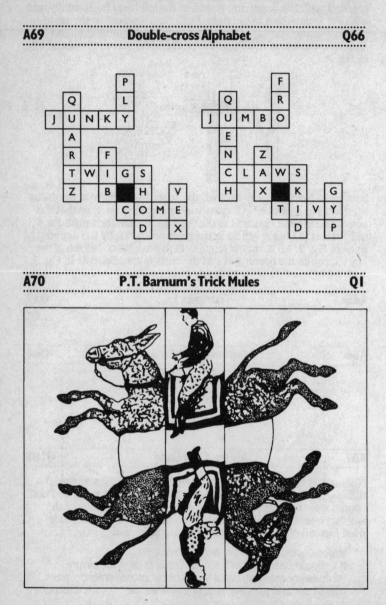

Construct a triangular pyramid.

A72   **Classic Kickself Introduction**

Polish

---

1. 12 onto 3
2. 7 onto 4
3. 10 onto 6
4. 8 onto 1
5. 11 onto 2
6. 9 onto 5

1854. The general formula is: $n!(1/2! - 1/3! + 1/4! - 1/5! \ldots + -1^n/n!)$. When $n = 7$, the value is 1854.

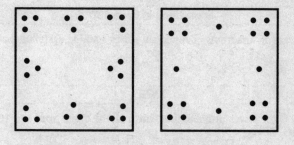

1. 24 bottles   2. 20 bottles

1. A little more than kin a little less than kind. 2. Tennis. 3. High IQ. 4. Disorderly conduct. 5. Short measure. 6. Centre of attraction. 7. Rearrangement. 8. Double park. 9. A turn up for the book. 10. Scatterbrain. 11. A snake in the grass. 12. A state of confusion. 13. Cardinal. 14. The Fifth Amendment. 15. Periodic. 16. Short list. 17. All in all. 18. Back street.

A total of 16 moves is necessary:

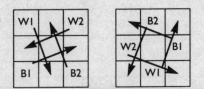

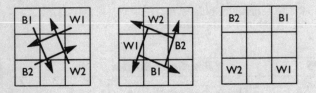

They are all anagrams of American states - Maine, Oklahoma and Utah.

2520 is the lowest number into which all the digits from 1 to 10 will divide.

Beginning with King Jovial, the diners were seated clockwise as follows: King Jovial, the Duchess of Dull Ness, the Marquis of Muttonfat, Mrs Toady, Lord Parsley, Queen Cilly, Lord Peekaboo, the Marchioness of Muttonfat, the Duke of Dull Ness, Lady Parsley, Toady and Lady Peekaboo.

The passenger who lives nearest the guard is not Petrov (4, 5). He does not live in Moscow or Leningrad, since, at best, these are only tied for being nearest to the guard (2). So he is not Ivanov (1). By elimination he is Sidorov.

Since the passenger from Leningrad is not Ivanov (1), by elimination he is Petrov. The guard's name is Petrov (3). Since Sidorov is not the fireman (6), by elimination he is the engine driver.

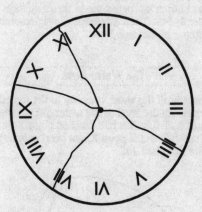

Each piece totals 20.

There were only three beneficiaries – son, father and grandfather.

24 miles; 06:30

A level mile takes ¼ of an hour, up hill takes ⅓ of an hour, down hill takes ⅙ of an hour. Hence, to go and return over the same mile, whether on the level or on the hill side, takes ½ an hour. Therefore, in 6 hours they went 12 miles out and 12 miles back. If the 12 miles out had been nearly all level, they would have taken a little over 3 hours; if nearly all up hill, a little under 4 hours. Hence 3 hours must be within ½ an hour of the time taken in reaching the peak; thus, as they started at 3, they got there within ½ an hour of 06:30.

'What hat's that?' said Bill.
'The flat hat,' said Ben.
'Oh, that hat,' said Bill.
'That's that then.'

For American readers we should explain that Bill and Ben were a couple of puppet characters, known as the Flowerpot Men, which appeared on a children's programme in the early days of British television in the 1950s. Their language closely resembled the 'flop lopy plop' dialogue of the coded text.

He tilted the butt until the water came up to the top edge without any running over. As the level of the water did not reach point X, the butt was not half-full. If it had reached point X, it would have been exactly half-full; but if point X had been submerged, it would have been more than half-full.

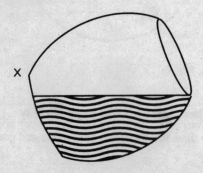

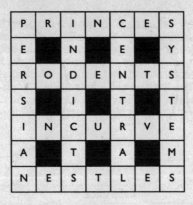

P	R	I	N	C	E	S
E	■	N	■	E	■	Y
R	O	D	E	N	T	S
S	■	I	■	T	■	T
I	N	C	U	R	V	E
A	■	T	■	A	■	M
N	E	S	T	L	E	S

A88   **Carousel**   **Q97**

Including Sammy, there were 13 children on the carousel, as can be seen from the diagram.

$\frac{1}{3} \times 12 = 4$

$\frac{3}{4} \times 12 = 9$

$4 + 9 = 13$

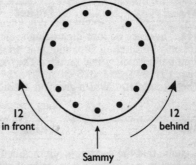

12 in front   12 behind

Sammy

A89   **Word Square**   **Q11**

When you successfully complete this puzzle you will have proved beyond doubt qualities of determination and patience.

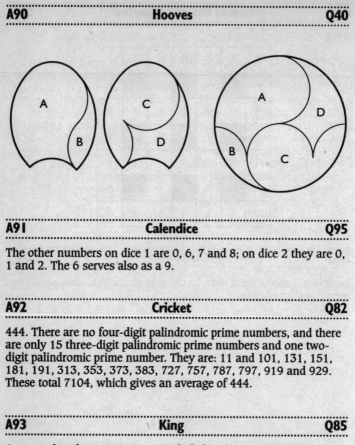

The other numbers on dice 1 are 0, 6, 7 and 8; on dice 2 they are 0, 1 and 2. The 6 serves also as a 9.

---

444. There are no four-digit palindromic prime numbers, and there are only 15 three-digit palindromic prime numbers and one two-digit palindromic prime number. They are: 11 and 101, 131, 151, 181, 191, 313, 353, 373, 383, 727, 757, 787, 797, 919 and 929. These total 7104, which gives an average of 444.

Assume that the servant is not included in the count. He arrives at the first manor with no men, so he would collect no men, and the final total would be no men. Therefore, the servant must include himself as the first soldier, and the numbers on leaving each manor increase in the progression 2, 4, 8 and so on. On leaving the thirtieth manor the total would be $2^{30} = 1073741824$.

When the clock says 12 hours 2 minutes and $29^{277}/_{288}$ secs.

On 1 July my watch gained on the clock 5 minutes in 10 hours –
i.e., ½ min per hour or 2 minutes in 4 hours. Hence, when my
watch said noon, the clock said 12 hours 2 minutes – i.e., the clock
was 3 minutes slow of true time, when the true time was 12 hours
5 minutes. On 30 July the watch lost on the clock 1 minute in 10
hours – i.e., 6 seconds per hour or 19 seconds in 3 hours 10 minutes. Hence, when the watch said 12 hours 10 minutes, the clock
said 12 hours 7 minutes 19 seconds – i.e., the clock was 2 minutes
19 seconds fast of true time, when true time was 12 hours 5 minutes. Hence, the clock gains, on true time, 5 minutes 19 seconds in
29 days – i.e., 319 seconds in 29 days – i.e., 11 seconds per day:
i.e., $^{11}/_{24 \times 12}$ seconds in 5 minutes

Hence, while true time goes 5 minutes the watch goes 5 minutes
and $11/_{288}$ seconds.

Now, when true time is 12 hours 5 minutes on 31 July, the clock is
(2 minutes 19 seconds + 11 seconds) fast of it – i.e., says 12 hours
7½ minutes. Hence, if true time be put 5 minutes back, the clock
must be put 5 minutes $11/_{288}$ seconds back – i.e., must be put back to
12 hours 2 minutes $29^{277}/_{288}$ seconds.
Hence, on 31 July when clock indicates this time, it is true noon.

---

729. To work out the answer, first draw up a table:

Range	Squares	Cube	Both
13-499	16, 25, 36, 49, 64, 81, 100, 121, 144, 169, 196, 225, 256, 289, 324, 361, 400, 441, 484	27, 64, 125, 216, 343	64
500-1300	529, 576, 625, 676, 729, 784, 841, 900, 961, 1024, 1089, 1156, 1225, 1296	512, 729, 1000	729

Possible true answers:
   1 and 2 – no, there are no cubes under 500
   1 and 3 – no, there are no squares under 500
   2 and 3 – yes, over 500 there is a square and a cube (729)

Janice = Peter, Susan = Alec, Helen = James

Call the artists D, E, M and S, and their vocations d, e, m and s. Then S must be d or m.

  1. If S = d, M = s or e; but if M = s, d is the namesake of M's vocation. So we have: S = d, M = e, E = s and D = m; for if E = m, the namesake of E's vocation is e.

  2. If S = m, M = d; for if M = e, E = d (impossible), and if M = s, E = d and D = e (impossible). So we have: S = m, M = d, E = s and D = e.

Therefore, collating (1) and (2), Mr Etcher is the sculptor.

Denote the names and occupations by letters (the names in capitals, the occupations in lower case) as follows: Baker A, a ; Brewer B, b ; Butcher C, c ; Carter D, d; Draper E, e; Ironmonger F, f; Painter G, g; Saddler H, h; and Smith K, k.

Then, (1) h is the father-in-law of f, and K has a married daughter. (2) H is engaged to g's daughter, who has rejected e and a, and D has an unmarried daughter. Therefore, as only two councillors have daughters, (3) K is h and D is g. Again, (4) E is a bachelor and is not e. (5) e's father is brother of Mrs A. (6) b and d are married to each other's sisiters; hence (7) A cannot be b or d.

Again we are given two relationships of the form:

(8) $\left\{ \begin{array}{c} D\ G\ X \\ g\ x\ b \end{array} \right\}$ and (9) $\left\{ \begin{array}{c} K\ H\ Y \\ h\ y\ d \end{array} \right\}$ where x and y are unknown

We also know that A is married; H and E are bachelors; f, b, d are married; a and e are bachelors; therefore H may be a, e, c or k. He cannot be e or k; he is therefore c. It follows in (9) that C is d.

Again b may be B, F or G; in (7) he cannot be A. But by (8) he cannot be B or G, and must therefore be F. It follows that G is f. We are only left with A, B and E, who must be a, e and k. Therefore, as A is married, he must be k, and hence by (4) E is a and it follows that B is e. Thus

    Mr Baker is the smith
    Mr Brewer is the draper
    Mr Butcher is the carter
    Mr Carter is the painter
    Mr Draper is the baker
    Mr Ironmonger is the brewer
    Mr Painter is the ironmonger
    Mr Saddler is the butcher
    Mr Smith is the saddler

2½ inches – i.e., through four covers and one set of pages.

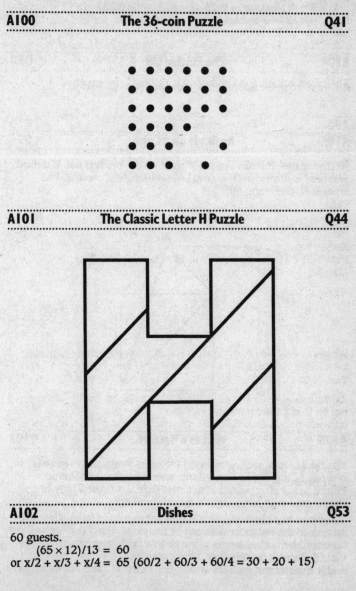

60 guests.

$$(65 \times 12)/13 = 60$$

or $x/2 + x/3 + x/4 = 65$ $(60/2 + 60/3 + 60/4 = 30 + 20 + 15)$

A103   Filling a Bath   Q61

3 minutes. This is solved by reciprocals in the form
$(6^{-1} + 4^{-1} - 12^{-1})^{-1}$ which is:

$\frac{1}{6} + \frac{1}{4} - \frac{1}{12} = 0.166 + 0.25 - 0.083$ $= 0.333$

     $1/0.333 = 3$ minutes

A104   The Elusive Lift   Q90

It was visiting the floors in the sequence of pi (3.141592).

A105   An Angle on a Cube   Q94

At first glance it looks like a 90° right-angle, but it is not. If a third
diagonal is drawn (AC), an equilateral triangle is created. The
answer is, therefore, 60°.

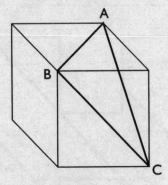

A106   Mad as a Hatter!   Q107

The riddle remained unanswered for many years and even today no
one can be sure what, if anything, was the intended solution.
Fifteen years after publication, Lewis Carroll, tongue firmly in
cheek, made the following whimsical comment.

'Enquiries have been so often addressed to me, as to whether any
answer to the Hatter's riddle can be imagined, that I may as well put
on record here what seems to me to be a fairly appropriate answer,
viz: "Because it can produce a few notes, that they are very flat;
and it is never put with the wrong end in front!" This, however, is

merely an afterthought; the riddle, as originally invented has no answer at all.'

However, several other suggestions have been ventured, notably by Sam Loyd who said, in true Carrollian fashion, 'the notes for which they are noted are not noted for being musical notes,' and he then went on to point out that 'Poe wrote on both' (our favourite solution) and that 'bill and tales are among their characteristics'. We will leave it to you, our reader, to choose for yourselves your favourite solution or to propose alternatives of your own.

A107   The Spider and the Fly   Q13

Diagram 4 shows that the shortest route is 40 feet. The spider crawls along five of the six sides of the room.

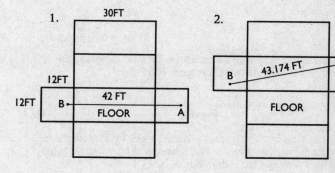

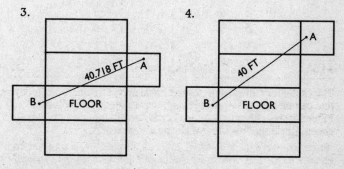

To solve this puzzle it is essential to pick up the opening clue that there were only two preliminary rounds. Therefore, the number of entries for one of the competitions must have been 4, 8, 16, 32, 64 and so on, so that no preliminary rounds were necessary. From there, by some trial and error, it is possible to arrive at the following solution, which is the only one that meets the requirements of the remainder of the puzzle.

Entries	Cube	Players in 1st round	Players in preliminary round	Preliminary round losers	Matches	My rounds
22	10648	10	12	6	21	5
32	32768	32	—	—	31	5
42	74088	22	20	10	41	6
	13					

Consolation event						
16		16	—		15	
					108	16

My handicap = 8; my wife's handicap = 16; club statistician's handicap = 13; Seth Arkwright's age = 108

Denote the girls by their initials and the judges by abbreviations. The following are the possible distributions of 10 votes among 6 competitors with not more than one 0:

a	6	1	1	1	1	0
b	5	2	1	1	1	0
c	5	1	1	1	1	1
d	4	3	1	1	1	0
e	4	2	2	1	1	0
f	4	2	1	1	1	1
g	3	3	2	1	1	0
h	3	3	1	1	1	1
j	3	2	2	2	1	0
k	3	2	2	1	1	1
m	2	2	2	2	2	0
n	2	2	2	2	1	1

Eight thought A the winner. This shows that distributions, *a, b, c, d, e, f, j* and *k* must have been used, giving A 34 points from eight judges. It is now clear that Ham's distribution must be *h*. The remaining distribution must therefore be *g*, as A's total is four times that of F. We can now see that the totals are: A 40, H 14, M 13, P 12, S 11, F 10.

Now it is clear that Eve's distribution is *a*, Bas's *c*, Lio's *b* and Vic's *g*, and it therefore follows that Geo's is *d* or *f*. F received 3 votes from Ham and 2 from Jim (either *e* or *k*), and she received 0 in three cases. As there are only six 0-votes altogether, the three given to F must have been given her by Vic, Eve and Lio; hence Geo's distribution is not *d* and must therefore be *f*. She therefore received 1 from each of the others. As Alec gave 0 to S and 1 to F, it is clear that his distribution must have been *e* (see P's remarks). Thus Jim's must be *k*.

Now we are left with *d* and *j* for Ste and Ted. In either case P must get 3 votes (1 and 2, or 2 and 1) from them; 3 from *d* would give her too great a total. Hence P receives 1 each from Vic and Lio to make her total right.

We now know that S must receive 3 votes from Vic and Ted, and as only 1 or 3 is available from Vic, since his 2 has gone to M, S receives 1 from Vic and 2 from Ted. Thus Ted's distribution must be *j*. To get P's total she must receive 1 from Ste, and to get M's total she must receive 3 from Ste and 2 from Lio. The table of distribution is accordingly as follows:

Distribution	c	h	g	k	e	d	j	a	b	f	Totals
JUDGE	Bas	Ham	Vic	Jim	Alec	Ste	Ted	Eve	Lio	Geo	
Annette	5	3	3	3	4	4	3	3	5	4	40
Helen	1	1	3	1	1	1	2	1	2	1	14
Mayblossom	1	1	2	1	2	3	0	1	1	1	13
Prudence	1	1	1	1	2	1	2	1	1	1	12
Sonia	1	1	1	2	0	0	2	1	1	2	11
Fern	1	3	0	2	1	1	1	0	0	1	10

Start at line 1 and finish at line 31.

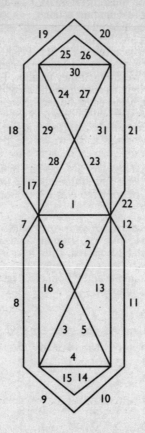

1. Alec Guinness. 2. Astronomical observations. 3. Christianity.
4. The countryside. 5. The desert oasis. 6. Desperation.
7. Disintegration. 8. A domesticated animal. 9. Good steel. 10. The
Holy Gospel. 11. In the South Sea Islands. 12. Knights of the Round
Table. 13. The landing of the Pilgrims. 14. The liquor habit.
15. Madam Curie. 16. Miguel Cervantes de Saavedra. 17. No tres-
passing. 18. The professional gambler. 19. Rome was not built in a
day. 20. The State of North Carolina.

The three operations are first to weigh coins 1, 2, 3 and 4 against 5, 6, 7 and 8; and then to weigh coins 9, 10, 11 and 4 against 1, 2, 3 and 8. There are now five possible actions.

1. If the scales were balanced both times, 12 is the counterfeit coin. Weigh it against another to see if it is heavy or light.

2. If the scales were balanced in the first weighing but not in the second, weigh coin 9 against coin 10 to see which tips the same way as in the second weighing. If they balance, 11 is the counterfeit and will be heavy or light as shown by the second weighing.

3. If the scales were balanced in the second weighing but not in the first, weigh coin 5 and against coin 6 to see which tips in the same way as in the first weighing. If they balance, 7 is the counterfeit and will be heavy or light as shown by the first weighing.

4. If the scales were off-balance the same way both times, weigh coin 4 against another coin. If they balance, the counterfeit is 8 and will be heavy or light as shown by the first two weighings.

5. If the scales were off-balance in opposite ways in the first two weighings, weigh coin 1 against coin 2 to see which tips as 1, 2 and 3 tipped in the second weighing. If they balance, 3 is the counterfeit coin and would be heavy or light as shown in the second weighing.

Multiply the first remainder by 70 ($2 \times 70 = 140$). Multiply the second remainder by 21 ($1 \times 21 = 21$). Multiply the third remainder by 15 ($6 \times 15 = 90$). Add the three results ($140 + 21 + 90 = 251$). Subtract 105 or its multiple from the sum, in this case its multiple ($251-210 = 41$ years old). Incidentally, Hyakugo-Gen in Japanese means 'subtract 105'.

$$1681\tfrac{1}{144} = \left(4\tfrac{1}{12}\right)^2$$
$$-5 = 961\tfrac{1}{144} = \left(3\tfrac{1}{12}\right)^2$$
$$+5 = 2401\tfrac{1}{144} = \left(4\tfrac{9}{12}\right)^2$$

The answer is not, of course, an integer.

The number of different solutions is 12 (as shown) and the number of pieces is eight. This is determined by the number of squares along the sides - i.e., a 4×4 square would require four pieces.